"You fell in love with me at first sight?"

Sharon felt numb. Had he really loved her?

"Not quite. But just about." Lee looked thoughtful. "But it's hardly important anymore. The girl I loved never existed outside my imagination."

Her sense of loss was like a knife twisting inside her. Lee had loved her! And she had killed his love.

"Oh, Lee," she said thickly, her eyes pleading. "I was lying when I said I'd married you for money. I wanted to hurt you because I'd been hurt. I was a little fool and I'm sorry—" Her voice faded. "You don't believe me, do you?"

"No," he said flatly. "I'm not sure what kind of game you're playing now, but there's no way you can turn yourself back into the girl I thought I married. We have a business arrangement. Let's keep it that way."

Other titles by

KAY THORPE
IN HARLEQUIN PRESENTS

Other titles by

KAY THORPE
IN HARLEQUIN ROMANCES

Many of these titles, and other titles in the Harlequin
Romance series, are available at your local book-
seller. For a free catalogue listing all available
Harlequin Presents and Harlequin Romances, send
your name and address to:

HARLEQUIN READER SERVICE,
M.P.O. Box 707,
Niagara Falls, N.Y. 14302
Canadian address:
Stratford, Ontario, Canada N5A 6W2

KAY THORPE

chance meeting

Harlequin Books

TORONTO · LONDON · NEW YORK · AMSTERDAM
SYDNEY · HAMBURG · PARIS · STOCKHOLM

Harlequin Presents edition published August 1980
ISBN 0-373-10378-6

Original hardcover edition published in 1980
by Mills & Boon Limited

CHAPTER ONE

ENGLAND in April. Watching the two children feeding the ducks a few yards away from where she sat, Sharon had to concede that Browning had known what he was talking about. When the sun chose to shine on budding trees and early spring flowers this oasis of central London became a minor Eden, lifting the lowest of spirits. For the first time since moving south from the northern town where she had grown up, she felt able to face the future with some real element of optimism in her soul.

The past winter had been hard and not a little lonely. More than once she had been tempted to sink her pride and go back to all she had been so eager to leave seven months ago. It was only the recurring memory of those final bitter words which had stiffened her backbone. Deep down she had always been aware of a certain lack of affection in Aunt Dorothy's attitude towards her, but it had taken sixteen years for the resentment finally to burst forth.

Lack of gratitude had been only one of the accusations levelled at her. Viewed in retrospect, it was possible to appreciate something of the emotions of a woman childless by choice who had felt morally bound to give up a well-paid job to take in her only brother's orphaned child, yet the fault had hardly lain with a six-year-old. Plenty of women managed to combine bringing up a child with an outside job, but in Aunt Dorothy's case the sacrifice had been total. Uncle Brian had suffered from that frustration too over the years; Sharon knew that now. A patient man, he had never complained, nor had he ever treated Sharon with anything but kindness, yet there must have been times when he wished his niece anywhere but in his home.

The chance to spend a year in the London office of the company for which she worked had seemed too good to miss at the time. If there had been any doubts at all, Aunt Dorothy's reaction to the very suggestion of her leaving Bolton put paid to them. 'All the money we've spent on you,' she had stormed, 'and now when you've only just begun paying a little of it back you want to go. Well go on, go! And good riddance!' Sharon had gone, with the firm intention of sending money each month in payment of the debt she owed, but she had found to her dismay that she needed the whole of her salary just to live on. Still smarting from the hurt inflicted, she wrote a stilted little letter informing her aunt and uncle that she would recommence payment the moment she was able. It was Uncle Brian who wrote back, denying any obligation and saying that her aunt had not meant half of what she had said, but he did not ask her to come home. At Christmas there had been a card and a gift token from both of them in Aunt Dorothy's handwriting, which seemed to suggest that the way might be open for some kind of approach, but Sharon had not been able to bring herself to make that effort as yet.

Spring was the time for new beginnings, she thought now on her park bench. Perhaps if she made the first gesture they could regain some kind of balance in their relationship. After all, they were the only family she had.

Putting up her hand to straighten a lock of hair tossed by the breeze, she caught sight of the time and gave a small gasp of dismay. She was already late back at the office, and she had only just finished clearing up last month's dues. Working to flexi-time rules had its advantages, true, but the temptation to spend that extra few minutes in bed on a cold wet morning generally ran her into owing hours. This month she had determined she was going to stick to a regular timetable if it killed her, and here she was after less than a week of it already breaking that vow.

The office was a good twenty minutes' walk away, the next bus due in ten, if she could get on it. Heading swiftly towards the park gates, she considered taking a taxi, and immediately abandoned the idea. Even if she could find one empty at this hour of the day, she could hardly afford that kind of extravagance just to save herself a few minutes. She was already in the red, so why not let it ride to the full hour? She could work that off tonight if needs be.

In spite of her decision, the sight of the bus coming along the road broke her feet into a run. Either her watch was slow or this was an extra service, but it was certainly the number she wanted and it seemed silly under the circumstances to be an hour late when she could perhaps cut it down to a half. The stop was a couple of hundred yards away and from what she could see of it there were only a couple of people waiting to board. With luck she should just about do it, especially if the driver happened to be having a good day and felt no temptation to set off just as the panting would-be passenger reached the doors.

There were a lot of people on the pavement, and mostly going in the opposite direction, thereby stopping her progress. Trying to dodge around one such figure, Sharon felt her ankle turn painfully under as her heel slipped on a stone, and was next moment down heavily on her knees with one involuntarily outstretched hand

breaking the fall. Tears springing in her eyes at the
smarting sting of grazed skin, she attempted to push
herself upright, and felt a firm hand come under her arm-
pit in assistance. The bus had reached the stop and its
doors were already closing again, adding frustration to
her embarrassment.

'That was a nasty tumble,' said a masculine voice
somewhere over her head, and she looked up with some
reluctance to meet her rescuer's eyes. They were grey, she
noted irrelevantly in that first brief moment. Right now
they held an expression midway between sympathy and
amusement, the former taking precedence as they
dropped to take in the state of her pantyhose below the
hem of her skirt. There was blood running down one leg,
mingling with the grit still clinging to her flesh beneath
the tattered nylon. Already she could feel both knees
stiffening, to say nothing of the hand she had used to
save herself which burned like fire. Surprisingly she
hadn't dropped her handbag; it was still clutched in her
other hand.

'I'm all right,' she managed in a shaken voice. 'Thank
you for ...'

'You're very far from all right,' he contradicted, making no attempt to release his hold on her arm. 'Those
grazes need attention.'

'I'll clean them up when I get back to the office,' Sharon
assured him, anxious only to be free of both the retain-
ing arm and the curious stares of passers-by. 'Really
I ...'

'You can hardly walk through the streets in that state,'
he said, breaking her off short once more. 'Look, my
car's parked just over here. The least I can do is give
you a lift.'

'It wasn't your fault,' she protested as he drew her
towards the gleaming silver Mercedes blatantly parked

on the double yellow line. 'You don't have to feel any obligation just because you picked me up. It was my own clumsiness that caused me to fall down in the first place.'

'I don't have time to argue about it,' he responded, opening the front passenger door and easing her down into the seat in one smooth movement. 'There's a traffic warden just coming round the corner. Fasten your belt and hold tight!'

He was round the front of the car and in the driving seat before she could move herself to obey the instruction, bringing the engine to throbbing life with one swift flick of the wrist and edging out into the afternoon traffic with the hard determination of one born to big city driving, ignoring the blare of a taxi horn as the latter vehicle attempted to block him off.

'There goes one frustrated lady,' he remarked on a note of humour, glancing in the mirror. 'She had her book out all ready too!' His eyes flickered swiftly Sharon's way when she failed to respond, taking in her inheld lower lip and cradled right hand. 'Hurting quite a lot by now, I'd say? All things considered, I think we'll call off at my place first and get you cleaned up properly. It's only round the corner.'

Sharon made no protest; she had a feeling it would have met with little success anyway. It was true too, her knees and hand were hurting enough to make her feel slightly sick. She stole a glance at him, seeing a firm profile under the crisply styled dark hair. His brows were heavy without being bushy, his nose high-bridged and jutting above a mouth which held a hint of sensuality along with the decisiveness in its line. His jawline was clean-cut, the skin of his throat unlined. About thirty, she guessed, and possessed of an assurance befitting his obvious stature. The jacket sitting so easily across broad shoulders had an expensive cut.

'Just around the corner' turned out to be an apartment block off Grosvenor Place. He left the car parked right in front of the main entrance and helped Sharon up the short but imposing flight of steps, keeping an arm about her waist as he pushed open one of the glass doors and ushered her through into a thickly carpeted vestibule. The uniformed man sitting behind a wood-panelled desk came swiftly to his feet on their entry, brows lifting in solicitous enquiry.

'Anything I can do, Mr Brent?'

'No problem,' came the easy reply. 'This young lady had a bad fall along the road back there. She needs first aid.'

A faint smile touched the other man's lips for a brief moment and was gone. 'Would you like me to fetch the box up?' he asked with what Sharon thought was a rather peculiar blandness. 'Won't take a minute.'

'No need, there's one in the apartment.' Firmly he eased Sharon into the lift and pressed the button, shutting out the doorman's dark blue-clad figure as smoothly humming mechanism sprang into action. 'Not going to pass out on me, are you?' he asked, eyes on her face as they moved upwards.

She shook her head, and forced a smile. 'I've never passed out on anyone yet, Mr Brent. It's really very kind of you to go to all this trouble.'

'It's no trouble,' he said. 'And the name's Lee.'

'Sharon Tiler,' she supplied. 'And I'm very grateful anyway.'

'We'll take it as read.' The amusement was in his eyes as well as his voice. 'Where were you going in such an all-fired hurry, did you say?'

'Back to work. It was my lunch hour.' Her tone was rueful. 'They'll be wondering what happened to me by now.'

'You can phone and tell them just as soon as we get your wounds seen to.' His arm came around her again as the doors slid open, his touch too thoughtfully gentle to be totally impersonal. Sharon closed her mind to the swift tensing of stomach muscle which signified physical awareness. He was a vitally attractive man, there was no denying that, but his interest in her was purely of the Samaritan variety. In a few minutes she would be on her way out of this place again, his good deed done.

The apartment took her breath on first sight. Outside of magazine illustrations she had never seen anything quite so luxurious before in her life. Vast acres of off-white, shag-piled carpet ran in all directions, scattered with long chesterfields and deep club chairs in a variety of colours and materials which all blended into the one composite scheme. Neither ultra-modern nor purely traditional in style, the huge lounge area struck a note entirely individual and somehow suited to the personality of its tenant. Picture windows looked out towards Green Park.

'This way,' her host said, and took her through a bedroom almost as big as the lounge, with an oval bed raised on a platform at the rear, to an adjoining bathroom three times the size of any other she had seen. The bath too was oval, but whereas the bed had been raised on a platform, this was actually sunk into one, the carpet covering the floor extending up the two steps to the very edge of the marbled porcelain. Bronzed mirror glass covered the two walls left free of fixtures and fittings. Sharon saw the two of them reflected there, one tall, dark and male, the other several inches shorter, with dark golden hair falling about a face totally lacking in the kind of glamour befitting a setting like this one.

'Pure fifties Hollywood,' commented Lee Brent with a somewhat rueful grimace, moving across to open up a

concealed cabinet behind the two inset basins. 'The
result of giving a designing friend too much of a free
hand while I was out of the country earlier this year.'
Whether the pun was intentional or not it was impossible
to say. His face when he turned back to her was devoid
of any readable expression. 'Luckily, she didn't have
time to start on the rest of the place before I got back.'
He gestured with the white box in his hand before setting
it down on the vanity unit to open it. 'You'd better take
your pantyhose off.'

Sharon hesitated only momentarily before deciding
that such extremes of modesty were a little out of place
in the circumstances. The pantyhose were ruined anyway. Certainly she couldn't go back to the office wearing
the remnants, although it was going to prove decidedly
chilly without any covering on her legs this early in the
year. While his back was still turned she swiftly slid them
down and off, conscious of the winter pallor of her skin
against the dark green of her suit skirt and a sudden sense
of vulnerability as her bare toes curled into the deep pile.

The smell of antiseptic made her nose wrinkle. Having
washed his hands in one bowl, Lee Brent took up cotton
wool and motioned her to a seat beside the other, then
bent and lifted her leg straight by the ankle, his grip
warm and firm behind her heel.

'It's going to sting,' he warned unnecessarily, feeling
her stiffen. 'Lift your skirt back a bit more or it might get
wet.'

Sharon did so, grateful that he had taken her tensing
for apprehension rather than involuntary response to his
touch. There was something unnerving about sitting
here like this with a man who was to all intents and
purposes a total stranger, regardless of his solicitude.

The bite of the antiseptic made her catch her lip
between her teeth to stop the exclamation of pain. Grip

tightening a fraction, he held the leg still while he cleaned out the tiny pieces of grit embedded in the graze, using fresh pieces of cotton wool in extravagant quantities. It took the steady drip of water on to the carpet to finally loosen her tongue.

'It's going to be soaked,' she said. 'Couldn't you put a towel down or something?'

'It will dry.' His tone was unconcerned. 'Keep still. There's just one more piece to come so far as I can see ... there!' He tossed the soiled wool into the waste bin and tore off another large chunk from the roll, which he handed to her unmoistened. 'Wipe round it with that while I tackle the other leg, then we'll see to your hand.'

Five minutes later, and to Sharon's infinite relief, he sat back on his heels in front of her to view his completed handiwork with a twist of humour about his lips.

'Not exactly a masterpiece,' he commented, 'but the best I can do under present circumstances.'

'You've done a marvellous job,' Sharon assured him swiftly, eager to be on her feet and out of this whole situation. 'I can't thank you enough!'

It was only then, as he lifted amused grey eyes to meet her own confused blue, that she realised he had been fully aware of her reactions to him during the whole time he had been ministering to her needs. He held her gaze for a long moment before dropping with slow deliberation to the region of her mouth, the mockery growing as colour crept faintly under her skin.

'There's no payment necessary,' he said. 'Unless you feel moved to any impulsive gesture.'

Fleetingly, and to her own astonishment, Sharon actually found herself tempted to meet that challenge, but the moment passed.

'I have to go,' she said jerkily.

'I'm not keeping you.' He got to his feet, the smile still

playing about his lips. 'I'll see if I can find you a pair of pantyhose.' Catching the flicker of expression in her eyes, he inclined his head. 'My sister sometimes uses the place when I'm out of town, and she leaves spares of everything around. Sit tight while I look.'

He was back within a minute, a cellophaned packet unopened in his hand. 'Thought so. They might not be your shade, but they're better than nothing.'

Better than *any*thing she was accustomed to, Sharon corrected mentally, catching sight of the brand name as he held out the packet to her. She shook her head in some uncertainty. 'I can't just walk off with your sister's things like that!'

'She'll never miss them. There's another dozen or so pairs where I got those from.' He dropped the packet into her lap when she still made no attempt to take it from him. 'For the Lord's sake put them on, will you! It's hardly warm enough outside to be going without. Do you want coffee – or something stronger?'

Sharon hesitated only a moment, aware of a hint of intolerance in his tone and recognising the inadvisability of trying his patience with any further protests. 'Coffee, please.'

'Right. I'll take a few minutes. Come on through when you're ready.'

Alone again, Sharon extracted the sheer, expensive tights and pulled them carefully over the two plaster dressings on her knees, an operation made all the more awkward by the graze on her hand which he had left exposed to the air. When she finally turned to view her face in the long mirror running above the dressing unit, she was dismayed to see the long smear of dust along her cheek. She looked a mess, hair all tousled from the breeze outside and not even a hint of lipstick left on her mouth. Small wonder Lee Brent had smiled so mockingly at the idea of kissing her! The kind of woman he would want to kiss was no doubt as far removed from Sharon Tiler as chalk from cheese.

It was pride rather than any desire to impress which instilled her to lightly touch up her make-up after cleaning her cheek, and draw a comb through her hair. With her shoes on she felt slightly more sure of herself, though not enough to stop the colour tinging her skin again when she went out to the living room and found Lee Brent already sitting there waiting with the coffee.

'Sorry I was so long,' she said on a light, bright note. 'I hadn't realised I was quite so dishevelled.'

He didn't bother to answer that one, indicating the chair set at right angles to his own as he poured coffee from the silver pot into china cups. 'Cream or milk?'

Some devil of perversity sparked in her as she took the seat. 'Do you have any Coffee Compliment?'

'Any what?' The blankness was not assumed.

'Powdered cream,' she substituted. 'It's what ordinary mortals use instead of the real thing. Doesn't turn sour.'

A glint sprang suddenly in the grey eyes. Without speaking, he set down the coffee pot and got to his feet, coming round the low table to where she sat.

Sharon resisted as he pulled her up to him, but it made little difference. His mouth was purposeful, forcing her lips apart, his hands hard against her back. Only when she stopped struggling and let herself go limp in his arms did he soften the kiss, drawing a response from her despite herself. There was firm muscularity beneath the cream silk shirt; she could feel the tautness through her fingers curved into his shoulders.

When he finally released her it was with obvious reluctance and by no means completely, his face and body still too close to hers for comfort.

'As an ordinary mortal,' he said very softly against her

hair, 'I've been wanting to do that for the last half hour. You have the loveliest pair of legs, even when they're smothered in blood and grit, or festooned with sticking plaster!'

Sharon pushed herself suddenly away from him, feeling the uneven thud of her heartbeat with a sense of shame. She had met this man for the very first time less than an hour ago, and she had allowed him to kiss her like ... that. Not only allowed but actually responded, too, if she were honest with herself. She couldn't bring herself to meet his eyes.

'I must go,' she said. 'I ... It's late.'

'It's twenty to three.' He hadn't moved, watching her with an enigmatic expression. His tone roughened a little. 'Come on, you weren't taken by surprise. You knew what was happening back there in the bathroom just as well as I did.'

There was little use in denying it, and she doubted if he would understand if she tried to explain that she had believed the attraction all on her side. The women he had known prior to this moment had all no doubt been both sharp enough and worldly enough to recognise arousal in a man without having to have it underlined for them. She attempted to bluff her way out of it instead with an assumed cynicism.

'So what am I supposed to do about it? Jump into bed with you right here and now?'

His shrug held deliberation. 'I wouldn't say no.'

'I'll bet!'

The inference was too heavily scored to be ignored. Sharon saw his lips tighten ominously and knew the shaft had gone home—a realisation which gave her small satisfaction. Here was a man too well accustomed to women in his bed, and she had given him little cause to suppose she might not be willing to join the line.

'There's no obligation,' he said. 'There'd have been no approach if you hadn't encouraged it.'

'*I* encouraged it!'

'That's right. If you'd been otherwise inclined you'd have told me what to do with the coffee and got straight out of here.'

Sharon was silent, not trusting herself to speak. After a moment she made herself reach down to the chair for her handbag, clutching it to her like some form of shield as she limped across the room. At the lobby door she paused, fishing recklessly into her purse for three pound notes which she tossed on to the nearest flat surface with a scathing gesture.

'That's for the tights!'

She half expected him to come after her, but he didn't. Waiting for the lift, she tried to control the trembling in her limbs with small success. Reaction, she told herself as the doors slid silently open. And guilt, conscience added. There had been more than a grain of truth in what Lee Brent had said back there: she had known what she was asking for if she stayed, yet she had still done it.

The doorman watched her exit from the lift with singular speculation, making her wonder just how many others he had seen pass the same way.

'Mr Brent not running you home, miss,' he asked. 'I can call you a taxi.'

Sharon shook her head, only too well aware that she could no longer afford a taxi fare after that last grand gesture upstairs. She was going to have to go to the bank again, and it was only Wednesday. Divided into weeks, her month's salary usually saw her through, but it allowed little leeway for gestures of any kind. Whatever she drew out extra this week must come out of next week's allowance, and that meant economising on something else. All the same she didn't regret the impulse. There had been considerable consolation in the expression on Lee Brent's face.

It was too late to go back to the office at all now. She would think of some adequate excuse in the morning. She took the tube out to Kennington, and then the bus to Blexley Road, finally letting herself into the bedsitter which was home with a wry little smile at the contrast between this and the apartment she had left. At least it was clean and reasonably furnished for what she was paying, she reminded herself. Her landlady was one of those who took pains to make things pleasant for her tenants.

There were two others, one on this same floor and another on the floor above. Both were young and male, students at the Polytechnic. Sharing a bathroom had proved fairly awkward at first until they had worked out a rota system – or until Sharon herself had worked one out. Neither of her fellow tenants had seen any particular difficulty.

Her floormate called in around seven on his way to his own room. At twenty, Greg Calvin was two years younger than herself, a cheerful extrovert with a friendly disposition which embraced all and sundry. Sharon had been glad of his companionship these last few months, aware that they each satisfied a need in one another for some kind of family attachment. If she had ever had a brother, she often thought, she would have liked him to have been something like Greg.

Viewing him tonight in the inevitable jeans and bomber jacket, she couldn't help comparing his appearance with that of the man she had met that afternoon. Hardly fair, she acknowledged at once. Given the same kind of background, no doubt Greg would have presented an equally finished picture. Anyway, the cowl did not make the monk.

He stayed only long enough to eat the supper for which Sharon had not felt in the mood, then took himself off to his own room to do the swotting even he dared put off no longer. The grazes still felt tender when Sharon went to bed at ten. She left the dressings in place for the night, and lay for an hour or more in the darkness trying vainly to stop her mind from going over and over the same ground before sleep finally claimed her.

No excuse was needed when she got to the office next morning, although it was suggested that a phone call would not have gone amiss. Apparently one of the other girls had been on top of the bus she had been trying to catch when the accident happened, and had seen everything from her vantage point.

'That was a really dishy man who got you up off the floor,' commented the latter at coffee break. Her grin was without malice. 'Bet he's always having women throw themselves at his feet! What happened after that? Last thing I saw he was leading you off with an arm round you. Some people have all the luck!'

'He dropped me off at the Underground,' Sharon improvised swiftly, not sure whether Maureen would have seen her getting into the car or not. 'I was in too much of a mess to think about anything but getting home.'

'Pity.' The other pulled a sympathetic face. 'You ought to have pulled a fainting fit or something—he might have given you mouth-to-mouth resuscitation.'

Sharon felt the warmth come into her face and laughed to cover up the telltale sigh. 'Trust you to think of that!'

'Well, you can't waste that kind of opportunity. They don't come along all that often.' Maureen paused in the act of turning away as some thought apparently struck her. 'You live on your own, don't you, Sharon?'

'Well ... yes.' Sharon was puzzled, wondering what
was coming. 'I have a bedsitter in Camberwell. Why?'

'Joan Barlow in Overseas is looking for somebody to
take over half of her place now that her apartment mate
got married. Thought you might be interested, that's all.'

'Well, thanks.' The reply was cautious. Hardly knowing the girl in question, Sharon felt doubtful. She knew
many people living away from the family home did
share in order to afford a better place, but there was
more to it than that. 'Perhaps I'll go and see her.'

She didn't in the end because the drawbacks were too
many and too obvious. She needed a bedroom of her
own, even if she did have to live in it and eat in it as well.
The Grosvenor apartment sprang in her mind's eye,
bringing a rueful smile to her lips. One thing was certain,
she would never aspire to a place like that except in her
dreams.

Another weekend came and went, bringing another
Monday morning and an unseasonable warmth to the
sun. Moved by some impulse she could not have explained, Sharon took extra care over her appearance that
morning, putting on a lightweight skirt and jacket in a
deep gold which lent toning highlights to her hair. Since
coming to London she had bought only essential items
of clothing, managing with the wardrobe she had brought
from home. The suit was one she had bought only a few
weeks before leaving Bolton, and she had not worn it
here before. She supposed she should save it for a special
occasion – except that such were unlikely to crop up. She
had been out with a couple of the younger men from
work, but neither relationship had progressed beyond
the occasional date because she hadn't wanted it to.

Coming through Accounts just before lunch, one of

the latter paused by her desk with an appreciative glance at the yellow suit.

'You look like a daffodil,' he remarked. 'Definitely springlike! What are you doing tonight?'

Sharon paused before answering, aware of what he was going to ask and not all that sure she wanted to spend the evening in Martin Dunn's company. Yet what was the alternative? Another long, lonely session in her room with a book? Martin was nice enough if hardly an exciting conversationalist. She should think herself fortunate.

'Nothing,' she admitted, smiling at him.

He smiled back, gratified. 'You are now. There's a good film on at the Odeon. Have you seen it?'

Sharon shook her head fatalistically. The cinema was the last place she wanted to visit on an evening such as this one promised to be, but it was Martin's money.

'Right, we'll grab something to eat first. Look forward to it.'

Maureen had been listening from the next desk. 'Does he mean he will or you should?' she asked dryly as he moved on, and Sharon laughed.

'Perhaps a little of both. Come off it, Maureen. Martin is all right.'

'If you're desperate—whoops, shouldn't have said that, should I?' Her glance held speculation. 'Are you?'

'Am I what?' Sharon asked, playing dumb.

'Desperate. He isn't your type, you know.'

Humour struggled against annoyance, and won. 'Really? What would you say was my type?'

'Oh, I don't know,' with a shrug, then brightening, 'Yes, I do. Somebody like that man who picked you up off the street the other day. Suave, sophisticated—and rich!'

She was being got at just a little, Sharon knew, though not with any real malice. She laughed again. 'Money doesn't make the man.'

'It does, you know. Especially when he's born to it.' The pause held deliberation. 'You were closer to him than I was. Would you say he'd been born to it?'

Sharon's throat closed up suddenly and inexplicably. 'I wouldn't have the slightest idea. I was far too busy nursing my grazes to take much notice.'

'Yes, you must have been.' The disbelief was unconcealed. Apparently Maureen had her own ideas regarding Sharon's absence that afternoon. 'Anyway, you're hardly likely to see him again.'

'No,' Sharon agreed on a tauter note, 'I'm not.'

They were both wrong about that. He was leaning against the nearside door of the silver Mercedes when she left the office block at five with Martin, wearing a suit almost the same colour as the car behind him. He straightened when he saw her, ignoring both the man at her side and the curious stares of others who had followed them out.

'Let's go,' he said, opening the passenger door.

Rooted to the ground, Sharon could only stare at him. It was left to Martin to break the silence.

'What's this about, Sharon?' he asked on a note of excusable bewilderment. 'I thought you were free tonight?'

'I was ... I am.' She pulled herself together with an effort, chin lifting as she held the grey gaze. 'I think you've made some mistake.'

The smile was slow. 'That's what we have to talk about. It's taken me long enough to find you. Do you get in the car, or do I put you in?'

Martin's face had gone stiff. 'Now look ...' he began.

'Sorry.' The other was unmoved. 'This is a matter between Sharon and myself.' His eyes hadn't left her face.

'You might have noticed I'm illegally parked.'

'You always are,' she retorted, and only registered the intimation when Martin made a small backward movement as if wryly acknowledging a prior right.

'My mistake,' he said. 'Goodnight, Sharon.'

Lee Brent raised an eyebrow as the younger man walked quickly away, his hand still on the car door. 'So?'

Conscious of Maureen's interested spectatorship from the doorway, Sharon took the line of least resistance and got into the car, sitting stiffly in her seat while he went round to slide in beside her. Only when they were moving away from the curb did she find it in herself to speak.

'I'm not sure what this is about,' she said stiffly, 'but whatever you've got to say it had better be quick!'

'Not right now,' he came back without turning his head. 'I've other things to think about. Just sit tight till we're out of this lot, then you'll have my full attention.'

'Where, out of this lot?' she demanded on a sharper note, and saw his lips twist.

'Somewhere public, don't worry. Relax, will you.'

Short of jumping out of the moving vehicle, there was little else she could do but sit back and wait until they reached their destination, wherever that might be. Sharon kept her eyes front, but nothing could cut off her awareness of him right there beside her. There was a faint tangy scent of aftershave mingled subtly with leather and polished wood. The car was custom-built, with every imaginable refinement—including, she was sure, fully reclining seats!

They finished up at a pub somewhere off Shaftesbury Avenue, leaving the car in a tiny cul-de-sac behind it where yellow lines were conspicuous by their surprising absence. Sharon had a vague impression of red leather and stone hung around with horse brasses as Lee Brent ushered her across the lounge bar to a quiet table on the far side. They had only just opened, she realised, and as yet were only just building up passing trade. Within an hour or so the whole place would probably be packed to the doors.

'Tonic,' she said when Lee asked her what she wanted to drink. 'It's too early for anything else.'

It may have been so for her; the hour certainly didn't appear to have affected his tastes, judging from the colour of the liquid in his glass when he came back from the bar. He made no attempt, however, to down it right away, rolling the glass slowly between his hands as he looked across the table at her.

'Before we go any further,' he said, 'there's a small matter of some money I have of yours. I won't give it to you here because it might be misconstrued by anyone happening to look in this direction, but when I do give it to you I don't want you handing it back, is that clear?'

'It wasn't for you,' Sharon retorted. 'It was to replace the pantyhose you gave me.'

'I know what it was for. As a gesture it hit right on target, if that's any consolation.' His tone was rueful. 'First time I ever got paid in my own coin, so to speak!'

The wind taken completely out of her sails, she gazed at him suspiciously, but there was no mockery in his expression.

'What I'm attempting to say in a rather roundabout fashion,' he continued, 'is that I miscalculated, and I apologise.' He sat back then with an air of having got a load off his chest, eyeing her quizzically when she failed to respond. 'Well?'

'I accept your apology.' She could scarcely do anything else, Sharon conceded inwardly, considering that her behaviour at the time hardly left her faultless. Shorn of righteous anger, she became suddenly uncertain of herself, and of him. She looked down at the glass in front of her, then back at him. 'How did you know where I worked?' was all she could think of to ask.

'There are ways and means. Does it really matter?'

'No,' she admitted.

'Then let's forget that part of it. Tell me about yourself instead.'

'Why?'

'Because I want to know.' He smiled at her expression. 'Genuinely. Whereabouts in the country do you come from? There's a faint accent, but not enough to put a finger on.'

His interest seemed real enough on the surface, but Sharon refused to be drawn beyond the barest of answers to his probing. Finally he desisted, his shrug light.

'You don't trust me,' he said. 'Can't say I blame you.' He offered cigarettes, lighting one for himself when she refused, and studying her thoughtfully through the curl of smoke as he slipped the gold lighter back into a pocket. 'Let's start again from scratch,' he suggested on the same light note. 'I'm Lee Brent, unmarried, heart-whole and fancy free, and I'd like very much to take you out to dinner.'

Sharon had to laugh, knowing as she did so that she had already capitulated. Whatever his motives, in this mood he was too irresistible to turn down.

She didn't remember the name of the place where they eventually ate, only that the maître d'hotel was French and Lee a regular enough customer to have his own favourite table. By then she had almost completely relaxed with him. Over coffee, and with only a little prompting on his part, she found herself telling him about Aunt Dorothy and the loneliness of her life here in London. He said little, but she sensed sympathetic understanding and warmed to it. When they danced on the pocket-handkerchief-sized floor, he put his cheek

down to hers as others were doing around them, and
held both her hands lightly against his chest, but made
no attempt to draw her too close. She wanted the music
to go on all night, conceding with the utmost reluctance
when he eventually suggested it was time to leave.

Despite everything, she still half anticipated an invitation to finish off the evening at his apartment once he had
her in the car, but he headed straight down across the
river. They neither spoke a great deal on the way out to
Camberwell. Sharon was fighting a growing sense of
depression. The evening had been wonderful, but very
soon it would be over and it was highly unlikely that she
would be seeing Lee again. Tonight had been his way of
making amends, that was all. Nice of him, only in many
ways it would have been better if he'd allowed her to
retain her previous image of him. Better for her, anyway.

She had a hand on her door lever ready to get out
almost before he brought the car to a standstill outside
the house.

'I've enjoyed it,' she said. 'Thanks.'

'Don't run away.' His tone was soft. 'How about tomorrow night?'

She turned her head to look at him in the light from the
nearby street lamp, keeping to her own side of the car.
'I don't think . . .'

'No strings attached. I just want to see you.' He put
out a hand and lightly traced the line of her cheek, smiling at her involuntary tremor. 'You're different, Sharon.
I don't think I ever knew a girl like you before.'

Her skin was tingling where his fingers touched her;
she wanted him both to stop and to go on at one and
the same time. 'How am I different?' she got out.

'I'll tell you another time,' he said. 'I'm booking you
for the week.' He paused, watching her face. 'Any objec-
tions?'

'I don't know.' She was hesitant, emotions confused. 'Lee ...'

'I told you, no strings. You set the pace. Do you like theatre?'

'Yes, I love it.' She forced a laugh. 'I can't very often afford it at today's prices.'

He ignored the last. 'Musical or straight?'

'Straight, but ...'

'I'll get tickets.' His hand had gone behind her neck, cupping her nape. Now he drew her towards him, bending his head to kiss her briefly and rather too gently on the lips. 'Does that reassure you?'

'Was it supposed to?' Her eyes were bright. 'I'm not *that* different.'

It was his turn to laugh. This time he gathered her closer, mouth more assertive yet still lacking that degree of demand she had first experienced from him. Sharon kissed him back honestly, knowing what she was probably getting herself into, and hardly caring right then. No man had ever affected her quite to this extent before. Just being with him made her feel all churned up inside.

'That's enough,' he said at length on an odd note. 'I'm only human. I'll pick you up at seven.'

She watched him drive off before going indoors, feeling the imprint of his lips still lingering on hers. Why Lee wanted her company was unimportant; the fact that he did was all that mattered at the moment. Take advantage of opportunity Maureen had said just a few days ago, and why not? She could always retreat if there seemed any danger of getting out of her depth.

CHAPTER TWO

IT was the beginning of a week she was long to remember. They went twice to the theatre, dined each night at a different venue, danced on one occasion till two in the morning and finished up drinking coffee at an all-night stand in Pimlico. By Friday, Sharon was owing the firm almost four hours flexi-time, and could still barely keep her eyes open when she arrived at ten.

'Serves you right,' observed Maureen judiciously from the adjoining desk. 'You can't burn the candle at both ends.' She paused then, eyes holding an expression Sharon found difficult to decipher. 'You didn't tell me who your boy-friend really was.'

'Yes, I did,' she denied, puzzled. 'Lee Brent.'

'Is that all you know about him?'

The other girl had come close to the truth there, although Sharon was not prepared to admit it. They had never once discussed Lee's own background, though they'd certainly covered most other subjects. She wasn't sure whether the omission was deliberate or not. Up to now it hadn't bothered her too much, she was bound to admit. There had been too much else to occupy her mind.

'Supposing you tell me what it is you think you know,' she countered, 'and I'll tell you if it's true or not.'

The newspaper clipping Maureen leaned across to toss on to her desk was dated a few weeks back. There was a large photograph of a wedding at the top with a write-up underneath. Lee's face leapt out at her from the left-hand side of the party, smile faintly twisted in the manner she knew so well. The bride seemed vaguely familiar, dark-haired and vivacious. She was wearing white, but with a large floppy hat instead of a veil and headdress. The fair-haired bridegroom Sharon had never seen before in her life, she was certain.

'So what?' she asked. 'He isn't the groom.'

'Read it,' Maureen insisted. 'Mom was clearing out last month's papers and I was going through them for an advert I wanted when I saw it. It's a family wedding. She's his sister.'

Well, she had certainly known about her, Sharon reflected in wry recall; she still wore a pair of her panty-hose. That was why the face seemed familiar, of course. She and Lee shared the same good looks, making allowances for the difference between male and female features. Lora, that was her name—now Lora Massey instead of Brent.

It took a moment for the rest to sink in. Brent Incorporated—heavens, was that Lee? Her glance sped back up the page and found the older man standing next to him, hair grey yet face bearing the unmistakable imprint. His father? Brent Incorporated. Where had she heard that before?

'You still haven't got it, have you?' Maureen sounded triumphant. 'He didn't tell you he owns the very floor we've got our feet on—at least, the Company does—along with heaven knows how many more office blocks right round the world. You've heard of the Brentwood hotel chain? That's them too. That's as far as I've got, but I'm sure there's more. They're property dealers in the widest sense possible—a multi-million dollar organisation, according to what I've been reading about them. His father is president. I imagine your Lee is next in line for the position, considering he's an only son.'

'He isn't my Lee.' Sharon's voice sounded thick in her ears. 'I've known him less than a week altogether. And what makes you so sure I didn't know all this already?'

'If I wasn't sure, the look on your face just now gave you away.' The other girl's tone softened sympathetically. 'Sharon, he's just amusing himself with you, can't you see that? You're hardly his type.'

'You thought I was not so very long ago.'

'That was a joke, and you knew it. He's in a position to have just about any woman he wants.'

'So why should he bother with a nobody like me?' Sharon finished for her, fighting to keep her voice steady. 'To be quite honest, Maureen, I don't really care why.'

'Yes, you do. You've fallen for him, haven't you? I don't blame you. He's really something.'

'But he's obviously only after one thing, and once he's had it he'll drop me like a hot potato—is that what you're trying to say?'

'Something like that, I suppose.' The other girl looked uncomfortable. 'Look, Sharon, I'm not criticising. If somebody like that took a shine to me I daresay I'd be just as overboard about it. He moves in a different world, that's all—more so than you probably even imagined.'

Only because she had never allowed herself to start imagining, Sharon acknowledged hollowly. She hadn't wanted to know, if she were to be honest.

'Sorry,' Maureen offered, watching her. 'Perhaps I should have kept my mouth shut. Are you seeing him tonight?'

'Yes.' Her tone was flat, her hands suddenly busy stacking the papers on the desk in front of her. 'It's almost time for coffee.'

The other girl took the hint and said no more, but Sharon found it difficult to concentrate on any work.

Yet why should any of it make a difference, when it all boiled down? She had been aware all along that it couldn't last. If tonight was to be her last date with Lee let it be a memorable one.

He came for her at eight as promised. Sliding into the now familiar car, she tried to conceal her emotions behind a bright façade. They were halfway into town before he said dryly, 'You're talking too much. What's on your mind?'

The pause was lengthy. Finally she had to say it. 'You should have told me.'

He didn't take his eyes off the road. 'Told you what exactly?'

'Brent Incorporated.' It came out like an accusation. 'Why *didn't* you tell me who you were, Lee?'

'You never asked what I did for a living. What difference does it make? You knew I wasn't any struggling office clerk.'

She flushed, sensing derision. 'No, that's my department.'

'That wasn't what I meant.' His glance held a hint of intolerance. 'Stop being so sensitive. I couldn't care less what kind of job you hold down. I've enjoyed your company these last few evenings, and I thought you'd enjoyed mine.'

'I have.'

'Then let's go on that way.'

Did she take that to mean he intended it to go on? Sharon wondered numbly. If so, for how long—and to what purpose? She sensed restraint in him every time he kissed her goodnight. When was he holding back for?

'Where are we going?' she asked in a subdued tone after a few minutes of silence.

The answer came easily enough. 'I thought we'd eat at my place for a change. I got the service restaurant to organise everything. It will be waiting for us when we get there.'

So there it was, the culmination of a week's preparation: a private candlelit dinner for two; soft music in the background. Probably champagne into the bargain.

So what? Sharon asked herself fiercely. If she was going to be seduced by anybody wasn't Lee Brent the answer to every maiden's prayer? She was in love with him, and love was supposed to transcend all doubts. If he wanted her badly enough to have gone to these lengths to set the scene then why not let matters take their own course? Whatever heartache might be in store for her afterwards she would at least have known some degree of closeness to him.

There was no one on duty at the desk in the lobby, to her relief. Going up in the lift she made every effort to act naturally. Certainly, Lee seemed to notice nothing amiss. If he remembered the few words they had had in the car he was ignoring them. As he had said, what difference did it make to their particular relationship?

The table was ready laid close by the huge sliding window, the view out over the evening-misted city magnificent. A heated trolley held their meal ready for serving, the main dish of duckling in orange sauce beautifully prepared and presented.

There were no candles, but with the dimmers down low the atmosphere was equally intimate. No champagne either, just a wine they had drunk together on a couple of occasions and Sharon had said she liked. She liked it now too, because it gave her some measure of confidence. As the evening progressed so did her resolve take firmer root. She loved this man, and if he asked her she was going to go to bed with him. She wanted to go. She wanted his lovemaking. It was like a storm growing inside her.

It was only when they'd finished eating and transferred to one of the long, low chesterfields to drink coffee and liqueurs that her mood began to change. Perhaps sensing it, Lee got up to change records on the stereo, pausing casually on the way back to where she sat to switch off another light.

'You get the best effect from the view in the dark,' he said.

Sharon tried not to stiffen as he slid an arm about her shoulders and drew her to him. It was only what she had been anticipating; he was running completely true to form. She parted her lips to his kiss, attempting to renew the desire she had been so much aware of earlier. It was there still, but submerged by a heavier awareness. The movement of his hand coming up slowly from her waist to her breast brought an odd mingling of need and rejection. She wanted his touch, his caress—but not like this. She was just an object to him; a challenge to be overcome.

Still holding her, he lifted his head to put his lips to her temple, pushing aside the hair until he found the tiny pulse beating there, taking his time, not rushing her—telling her without words that they had all night. When he did speak it was almost an intrusion.

'I know it's been less than a week,' he murmured, 'but I can't wait any longer. Sharon ...'

'No!' She put both hands flat against his chest and pushed him suddenly away, jumping to her feet in the same action. '*No*, Lee. I ... changed my mind.'

He didn't move for a moment, expression difficult to decipher in the near darkness.

'I wasn't aware you'd ever made it up,' he said on an odd note. 'Don't you think you should hear the question before you decide the answer?'

'I know what you were going to say.' She was holding

herself rigidly in check, wanting badly to snatch up her things and get out of here before he stirred himself to take hold of her again, yet conscious of a need to let him know just the way she felt. 'I've known all week what you were building up to. You looked me up with the one intention, didn't you, Lee?'

His smile was unexpected. 'I looked you up with some intention, yes. I wasn't totally sure what it was myself until a couple of nights ago.'

'Do you expect me to believe that?'

'No,' he admitted. 'You're obviously not in any frame of mind to believe anything I say at the moment.' He came to his feet before she could move out of reach, blocking her way of escape. His hands were firm on her shoulders, making her face him; the grey eyes unavoidable. 'Sharon, if all I wanted was to take you to bed we'd be there now.'

She stared at him, not understanding. 'Then what . . .'

'I'm asking you to marry me,' he said.

Her breath came out on a long, slow sound, her body losing its rigidity. The glow started deep, running through her like quicksilver to shine out of her eyes. 'Lee . . .'

'So answer me.' It was a superfluous command and he knew it, mouth tilting even as he said it. 'Yes, or no?'

The shock was still in her but there was no doubting his seriousness, even smiling the way he was. Her reaction was enough to make anyone smile, she thought dazedly. She had been so certain of his motive in bringing her here tonight. 'Yes,' she said. 'Oh, yes!'

'That's all right, then.' There was satisfaction in his voice. He swung her up off the floor and sat down again on the chesterfield behind him, holding her across his lap with her face on a level with his shoulder. His mouth on hers was possessive, setting her alight. She slid her arms up about his neck and clung to him, kissing him back almost feverishly, her whole mind centred on the thought of a future spent like this with Lee. *Mrs Lee Brent*—how wonderful that sounded! She still couldn't quite take it in.

Her breath caught a little in her throat as he slid a hand in under the V-neckline of her dress. His fingers were warm, supple; gentle, yet so exquisitely agonising in their touch against her skin. He knew just how to touch—and where—making her gasp against his lips. When he unfastened the three tiny buttons in order to ease back the material covering her, she made no attempt to stop him, but some slight increase in bodily tension must have communicated itself to him, because he lifted his head to look at her.

'What is it?' he asked on a low note, leaving his hand where it was. 'What's worrying you?'

'Nothing.' She tried to sound sure of it.

'Don't you like being touched this way?' he insisted, recognising the uncertainty despite her efforts. 'Am I hurting you?'

'No.' She put her own hand over his as if to emphasise the denial. 'And yes, I do like it. It's wonderful. Only ...' She hesitated, not even sure what it was she was trying to say. 'Lee, I want you to make love to me, it isn't that. I just can't ...'

'You just can't let yourself go with me because you still have a suspicion that proposal I made you was an excuse to get you to do just that,' he finished for her on a flat intonation. 'Do you really think I'd go to that amount of trouble for a single night's pleasure?'

'No, I don't suppose so.'

'Then stop being a little idiot. We're going to be married whatever happens.'

'Why me?' she burst out suddenly. 'You could have anybody you wanted, Lee. Why me?'

Some change of expression flickered in his eyes. 'Why do you think?'

'I'm not sure.' She paused, made herself go on. 'You haven't even mentioned the usual reason.'

'You mean I haven't said I love you.' He smiled a little. 'That's probably because I took it for granted you'd know. I never proposed marriage to anybody before. You'll have to forgive me if I don't follow the book.'

In that moment she could have forgiven him anything and given him everything. It was Lee himself who did the drawing back this time.

'No, you're right—it's worth waiting for.' The pause held some element she wasn't sure of. 'I hope you won't mind a fairly quiet wedding. We only just went through one load of pomp and ceremony for my sister. I don't think I could take it as a central figure.'

Sharon didn't think she could either. Not in the circumstances. She said hesitantly, 'Lee, what about your family? How will they react?'

'My father will be highly delighted. He thinks it's past time I settled down.'

'But will he approve? Of me, I mean?'

'Why shouldn't he approve?'

'Well, I'm not . . . from your world.'

'In your mind, not in mine. What creates the difference —money?'

'Not altogether.' Her glance encompassed the darkened room, coming back to the window and the sparkling view framed there. 'Environment mostly. You've lived this way all your life; to me it's like another planet.'

'You'll soon adjust. It's all a matter of perspective.' He made a small impatient gesture as she started to

speak. 'Forget it. It isn't important unless you make it
so yourself. You'll meet my father tomorrow—no, make
it Sunday; it's the only day he ever relaxes.' He studied
her for a moment, dropped his glance to the hand still
covering her breast, and wryly removed it to refasten the
three buttons. 'I'd better take you home.'

Sharon wanted to stay, but she couldn't bring herself
to say it. She needed time on her own to think straight
again. She was going to marry Lee. It still didn't seem
real. She had known him so short a time. Could love
really happen that way? Yet it had happened to her, so
why not to him? And what other reason could he have
for wanting to marry her?

It still wanted fifteen minutes to midnight when Lee
drew up in Blexley Road. He left the engine running
while he kissed her goodnight.

'I shan't be able to see you tomorrow,' he said. 'I'll
be out of town all day and most of the evening. I'll pick
you up about eleven Sunday morning.' He seemed detached, almost withdrawn, lifting a brief hand in farewell as she turned on the pavement, and moving off
straight away.

The feeling of unreality persisted all through Saturday,
interspaced with bursts of pure elation. During one of
the latter periods, Sharon pressed a fresh white blouse to
go with her yellow suit, and polished her only decent
leather handbag until it looked like burnished bronze.
If Mr Brent was anything like his son she had nothing
to worry about, and if he wasn't—well, Lee loved her.
Armed with that knowledge she could face anything.

He was dressed casually in slacks and a beige wool
sports jacket when he came for her, a scarf tucked into
the open neckline of his cream shirt. He both looked
different and seemed different from the man she had
known this past week. She felt tongue-tied with him.

They were heading south on the Bromley road before he commented on her monosyllabic responses to his attempts at conversation.

'Had regrets?' he asked.

'No.' She gave him a sidelong glance, suddenly aware of what really was troubling her. 'I thought you might have.'

His smile held reassurance. 'No way. Father's expecting us. I didn't intend dropping you on him.'

'You've told him?'

'I've told him.'

Sharon waited, forced into asking when he failed to add to the statement, 'How did he take it?'

'Right on the chin.' The laugh was dry. 'He's looking forward to seeing you.'

'I hope so!'

'Don't start that again. He'll take you on merit. Give him the impression you don't have much self-esteem and he's hardly likely to disagree with you!'

'It isn't a lack of self-esteem,' she denied with some heat, and saw his mouth turn down at the corners.

'Confidence, then. That aunt of yours has a lot to answer for. Have you contacted her yet?'

'No,' Sharon admitted.

'Then do it tomorrow—unless you'd like to phone from the house?'

'I'll wait till tomorrow.' She quickly changed the subject. 'What did you say the house was called?'

'White Ladies—Dad's a Dornford Yates fan. Did you ever read the Berry books?'

'One, I think. Funny, but awfully dated.'

'The gentry as they used to be. Those times won't come again. Not that the Brents were part of it. People in trade were looked down on by the upper classes in those days.'

'Property speculation can hardly be called a trade.'

'We buy and sell—what else would you call it? My grandfather started the ball rolling when he bought a plot of land on what was the outskirts of the city in the early twenties. A man of foresight.'

'And now you're world-wide,' she murmured, and felt his swift glance.

'Been doing some homework?'

'Not me, a friend.'

'The same one who convinced you I was only after the one thing?' He didn't wait for an answer. 'So I was, but not with the same object. You do realise it's going to be a pretty short engagement, I hope?'

'Is it?' Her laugh was self-conscious. 'I don't even feel engaged!'

'That can soon be altered.' There was a layby sign-posted on their side of the road. Lee drove into it, bringing the car to a halt behind a screen of trees. 'Open your glove compartment,' he said.

Sharon did so tentatively, gazing at the small, leather-covered box with a throat gone dry. When she made no further move, he reached across her to take it out, flicking back the lid to reveal the antique diamond nestling inside.

'It was my grandmother's,' he said. 'It should fit, she was just about your build. If you'd prefer a modern ring, we can always go and choose one next week, of course.'

'Oh no! No, this is beautiful!'

'Good. She left it for this purpose. Give me your hand.'

Sharon did so, quivering to the touch of his fingers as he slid the ring on. 'It fits perfectly,' she said on a breath-less note.

'Now it's official.' There was something in Lee's tone which drew her eyes swiftly to his face, but his expression revealed nothing out of the ordinary. 'We'll make it a

May wedding. Considering your lack of close family, it would obviously be more convenient to have it here. Your aunt and uncle can travel down.'

'They may not want to,' she said uncomfortably. 'I told you how Aunt Dorothy feels about me.'

'You told me what she said she felt on one occasion. We all do and say things on the spur of the moment that we regret later on. You can't write off sixteen years at a stroke, Sharon. Ask them.'

'I will.' She paused. 'You seem to have everything already thought out.'

'Do you object?'

She wasn't sure whether she did or not. Lee was accustomed to taking charge, that was apparent. Would he expect to organise her life in the same way? She was being ridiculous, she decided in the same moment. All he'd done so far was apply some common sense. She shook her head, smiling at him. 'No, of course not.'

White Ladies stood in its own grounds half a mile outside the village of Branley Heath : a graceful house, its walls rendered white beneath a green tiled roof. The copse of silver birch trees standing off to one side added further support to the choice of name. Daffodils massed the flower beds flanking the drive.

Inside there was warmth and quiet luxury. If houses possessed atmosphere—and Sharon thought they did— this was a contented one. She felt at home there immediately. A conservatively dressed woman in the mid-fifties came out through a door at the rear of the large, square hall, pausing when she saw the two of them.

'Good morning, Mr Brent,' she said formally. 'Your father is in the library. He asked for you to go on through when you arrived.'

Lee put his hand lightly on Sharon's arm. 'This is Mrs Reynolds, my father's housekeeper.'

Sharon was aware of swift appraisal and an even swifter summing up. She saw surprise flicker for an instant in the other's eyes, but her voice was without particular inflection as she said: 'I'd like to offer you both congratulations.'

'Thanks.' The acknowledgement sounded a little abrupt. Lee turned towards a door on the right, drawing Sharon along with him. 'Come and meet my father.'

The library appeared to be part study too, with a desk set at an angle across the far corner and only one wall lined with bookshelves. The man standing at the window turned on their entry and stood looking at the two of them for a moment before moving forward. He was older than she had thought from that newspaper photograph, Sharon realised, but his features had retained their firmness under the iron-grey hair. This was what Lee himself would look like at sixty or so if he kept himself in the same trim. There was an equal lack of spread beneath both waistbands.

'So you're the wonder woman who finally bowled this son of mine over,' he said assessingly to Sharon. 'That was quite a bombshell he dropped last night on the phone!'

'I don't see why,' put in Lee. 'You've been telling me I should find myself a wife for years.'

His father's glance was dry. 'I've been telling you a whole lot of things for years, and damned all difference it's made! I only hope you know what you're taking on, Sharon.'

'I think so.' She hoped she sounded more confident than she felt. She attempted to lighten the moment with humour. 'It's supposed to be for better or worse, after all.'

He laughed, taking new stock of her. 'That's true. He's a lucky man if you can see it that way. Too many want out the minute the going gets a little rough.'

'What are you trying to do?' his son demanded without undue concern. 'Put her off the whole idea?'

'No, just making sure she has the true picture.' He looked back at Sharon and shook his head. 'Don't let that surface charm fool you. He's as hard-headed as they come. Man like that could be hell to live with.'

'Were you?' she asked without conscious guile. 'You're very much alike.'

It was Lee's turn to laugh, expression sardonic. 'Pity Mother isn't here to answer that question—it might have made interesting listening!'

His father didn't turn a hair. Apparently the former Mrs Brent had been gone long enough for the mention of her name to elicit little pain. Sharon's retort had taken him a little aback, but he appeared to suffer no resentment. 'I think you might be good for this family,' he said on a note of amusement. 'Come and have a look round the gardens before we have lunch and you can tell me all about yourself. All I got from him last night was "wait and see".'

The appealing glance Sharon directed towards Lee met with little response. Obviously he was leaving it to her to fill in the details of her background. Because he knew how his father was likely to react if he told him himself? Richard Brent seemed to like her so far, but how would he feel when he realised how lacking in all the qualities he no doubt considered essential in his son's future wife she really was?

Lee accompanied them no further than the long rear terrace, taking a seat on the stone bench which formed one corner and leaning his back against the ivy-covered wall behind him with the obvious intention of staying put.

'I've seen the gardens before,' he said on a lazy note.

'You two carry on and pick me up on your way in to lunch.'

'Leave him,' Richard Brent advised as Sharon made to say something. He tucked her hand under his arm with a smile. 'We'll do better without him.'

The sun had enough warmth in it to have made the walk very pleasant, if Sharon had not had other matters on her mind. She barely waited until they were out of Lee's hearing before blurting out what she felt she had to say.

'Mr Brent, before you start asking me any questions about my background, etcetera, I think you ought to know I don't have one—at least, not the kind you're probably thinking of. Lee should have told you.'

There was no visible reaction in the strong features, nor any change in pace. 'What should he have told me exactly?'

'That I work in an office in town—in a building you own, actually—and my people were working class.'

'Were?' The inflection told her nothing.

'They were killed in a house fire when I was six. Dad got me out, but Mum was trapped in a bedroom and he went back for her. At least, that's what I was told. I don't remember much about it.'

'Who brought you up?' he asked.

'My father's sister.'

'Also working class?'

Her chin lifted a fraction. 'Yes. Uncle Brian is a shop foreman.'

'I see.' The pause was lengthy. 'How does Lee feel about all this?'

'He told me it was all in my mind and to forget it.'

'In other words, it's immaterial to him. Did he suggest I might feel differently?'

'No,' she was bound to admit. 'But ...'

'But you took one look at me and decided I was a likely candidate for social snobbery.' His tone was measured. 'A few minutes ago I'd have said that Lee had found himself a girl with something about her. There's nothing in what you've told me to change that opinion, but I could be wrong. One thing I don't like is having my attitudes predetermined.'

'I'm sorry.' She hardly knew what else to say.

'So you ought to be. I'm only interested in my son making a lasting marriage. Do you love him?'

'Yes,' she said softly. 'Oh, yes, I do!'

He searched her face, then nodded as if satisfied by what he saw there. 'That's the most important ingredient. He's a fortunate man. How did the two of you meet?'

Sharon told him, omitting certain details, and glanced up when she had finished to surprise an odd expression on her companion's face.

'So you've actually known Lee little more than a week,' he said. 'That was a very swift decision on both parts.'

'It happens like that sometimes, doesn't it?' Sharon murmured. 'At least, it did for me. I could hardly believe Lee felt the same way.'

'Yes,' on a dryish note. 'He always did believe in moving fast once he'd set his mind on a course of action. At thirty-two it may take him a time to settle down to married life, my dear, but I'm sure you'll cope.'

Sharon laughed. 'We're not married yet!'

'But you're going to be—and soon.' His tone was firm. 'We'll get a date settled today while you're here.' He hesitated briefly. 'You'll want to be married in your own part of the world?'

Sharon shook her head uncomfortably. 'It could be difficult. I left home under some misunderstanding. Lee thinks it will be better if we get married down here—

just a quiet wedding, probably at the register office.'

'No, not a register office,' with emphasis. 'Lee gets married in church as his sister did!'

'Will you tell him that?' Sharon ventured after a slight pause, and he smiled suddenly.

'I'll tell him. My housekeeper and my personal secretary can do all the arranging between them. The first thing they'll want from you is a list of guests.'

The speed at which matters were progressing took Sharon's breath away. Apparently Lee was not the only Brent who moved fast once a course of action was decided upon.

'There's only Aunt Dorothy and Uncle Brian,' she said on a hesitant note. 'And I'm not even sure they'll want to come under the circumstances.'

'If they don't,' he said, 'they're hardly worth considering as family. Try them anyway. And you must have some friends.'

'No really close ones. One or two people I work with, perhaps.'

'Well, I'll leave that to you. I daresay our side will make up for any shortage.'

'Mr Brent,' her voice was low, 'when Lee suggested getting married down here I don't think he meant an affair like you gave his sister—and I certainly don't expect it.'

'We'll discuss it,' he interrupted, not unkindly. 'It's just on lunchtime. Let's go back to the house.'

Lee was waiting for them in the same place. He smiled when he saw them coming.

'Did you straighten her out?' he asked his father.

'I think you could say we reached a fair degree of understanding.' Richard gave his son an assessing look. 'Sharon was telling me how the two of you met.'

'Was she now?' The response revealed little. 'Fate

steps in at the most surprising moments.'

There was something in that brief exchange which bothered Sharon a little, although she could not have said why. She was relieved when the sound of a gong struck in the house announced the meal.

'A bit pretentious,' Richard commented on a humorous note, leading the way. 'But staff is so difficult to come by these days, and it's easier than having Mrs Reynolds search the grounds every time she needs to remind me what the time is.'

'She looks after the house entirely on her own?' Sharon asked, thinking that must be a considerable task with a place the size of White Ladies.

It was Lee who answered. 'With the help of three domestics from the village. She isn't so hard done by.'

'You never did care for her much,' acknowledged his father, sounding undisturbed by the fact. 'I can't think why. She's very efficient.'

'Too much so. She runs the place like a hotel.'

'Considering you're only rarely in it I hardly see why it matters to you,' on a mild note. 'Have you thought about where you're going to live after you're married? Your apartment is adequate as a *pied-à-terre* but hardly for a family.'

'Aren't you running a bit far ahead?' Lee sounded amused, his eyes on Sharon's face. 'There's going to be plenty of time to start a family.'

'You never know. Besides, this is something which affects all of us.' Richard stopped at the open french doors leading back into the library, his glance going from one to the other. 'I've been thinking about giving up the house for some time now. It's too big for one man. Lora and Jason have Copperlea, of course, and as you showed little sign of finding yourself a wife ...' He paused, eyes holding those of his son with equal steadiness. 'Well, what I'm suggesting is that I make over White Ladies to you both as a wedding present.'

Silence followed his offer; on Sharon's part, at least, because she was too stunned to find immediate words. This beautiful house, theirs to live in; those grounds to wander through, sit in, look at and enjoy. A paradise for children, she thought, and felt a quiver run through her at the idea of bearing Lee's child.

She became aware that both men were watching her, the elder with understanding, the younger with an expression she found vaguely disturbing. Lee was the first to speak, tone level.

'Obviously you like the idea.'

'Who wouldn't?' The warm light was still there in her eyes as she looked at him. 'Oh, Lee, I can hardly take it in!' Her glance switched to Richard as another thought struck her. 'But where . . . I mean . . .'

'I'd be moving out, naturally.' He was smiling, not in the least put out by the implication in her hesitancy. 'I may decide to live at my club in town. I'm not sure yet.' To Lee he added smoothly, 'What do you say?'

His son's shrug was light. 'What can I say, except thanks. You won't object if we do it over to our own tastes?'

'Oh, but it's perfect as it is,' Sharon broke in, not wanting her future father-in-law to imagine his tastes judged wanting. 'Just perfect!'

'You've hardly seen any of it yet.' Lee's tone was almost brusque for a moment. It lightened again under her swift glance. 'I'll show you round after lunch.'

'I'd like that.' She looked up shyly at Richard. 'Thank you. That must be the most wonderful wedding present anyone ever received!'

He laughed. 'Sheer laziness. Saves me cudgelling my

brains for something else. And it's nice to think White Ladies is going to stay in the family.'

Sharon was a little concerned about Lee's quietness during lunch. He made no demur when his father suggested a date some four weeks ahead for the wedding, and simply lifted a sardonic eyebrow at the statement that it should take place in the village church.

'You seem to have everything well sorted out,' was all he said.

Sharon waited until later when they were alone before saying tentatively, 'Lee, I've no objection to a register office wedding if you'd prefer it.'

He eyed her for a moment with an odd expression. 'What about your preferences?'

'I told you, I really don't mind.'

He smiled then, and shrugged. 'It's all the same in the long run. The church will certainly suit my mother better. She'd be too concerned about what people might think otherwise.'

Sharon's head jerked up in sudden bewilderment. 'I thought your mother was dead.'

'Sorry if I gave you that impression. They've been living apart for the last ten years—since they found it impossible to live together any longer.'

'They're not divorced?'

'No. Apparently neither ever felt the need. She's out of the country at present, so you'll not be meeting her for a week or two.'

Sharon could only feel relieved at the last statement. She badly needed some breathing space. 'So both you and your sister stayed on here at White Ladies?' she ventured, and received another of the dry smiles.

'At twenty-two if I'd moved at all it would have been to a place of my own. Lora was only fifteen and a different proposition. She went with Mother. You think my father and I are alike—wait till you see Lora and my mother together. They're more like sisters than mother and daughter.'

Illogically, Sharon found herself wishing there were only Lee and his father to think about. Lora and her mother were unknown quantities. On the other hand, Lora herself was only just recently married. Surely she would realise the stresses and strains of the situation.

The house was even larger than she had first imagined, with eight bedrooms in addition to the long billiards room on the upper floor. Half the bedrooms had bathrooms en suite, each of the latter tiled to match the colour scheme of the adjoining room. These were never changed, Lee explained, but simply renewed when necessary so that each room bore the name of its scheme in perpetuity. One of the things she might like to think about altering, he added without undue interest. Tradition obviously meant little to him.

Back on the ground floor again, he showed her the magnificent drawing room with its graceful Adam-styled fireplace and velvet curtains, flanked by a smaller sitting room furnished in a feminine style in soft blues and greys.

'My mother's,' Lee said briefly. 'Nobody else came in here without invitation.'

Sharon made no comment. The room she liked best of all was at the rear of the house, opening again on to the terrace and holding a white Steinway piano in addition to its complement of brocade sofa and chairs. Angling in, the afternoon sun lent a golden glow which welcomed.

'Does anyone play it?' she asked on a casual note, viewing the closed lid and empty rack.

'Not me,' Lee denied. 'Father used to, but I haven't heard him for some time now.' He paused, glancing at her. 'Do you play?'

'A little.' She smiled. 'Aunt Dorothy insisted I start taking lessons when I was seven, and I turned out to have something of an aptitude for it. Never on a concert grand, though.'

He went over and tried the lid. 'It's open. Play something for me now.'

'Now?' She was suddenly sorry she had made any claim. 'Well, I ...'

'Do you have to be in some special mood?' on a note which made her flush.

'No, of course not,' she denied, and tried to pass off the moment's discomfiture with a touch of humour. 'I'm not nearly good enough to indulge in artistic temperament. What kind of thing do you like?'

'You choose. Music isn't my particular forte. I like listening, but I'm not always sure what I'm listening to.'

He sat down in a nearby chair as she took her seat on the stool, crossing one leg over the other knee with an air she thought might hold a hint of resignation. The notion put her on her mettle. Indulgence, no matter how well meant, was not what she wanted from him.

The first crashing chords of the Warsaw Concerto had exactly the effect she sought, jerking up his head as if it were attached to a wire. Mouth curving, she relaxed and began to get the feel of the instrument. It was several months since she had last played anything, and the rendition was by no means faultless, but the sheer delight in playing at all was almost enough.

Richard was standing in the doorway when she looked up on finishing, an amused speculation in his eyes.

'Spectacular,' he commented. 'Now play something to soothe rather than startle.'

'That was for my benefit.' Lee sounded amused too, a glint in the grey eyes. 'To take the wind out of my sails, as it were. Do as he says, Sharon, and play the thing properly.'

She smiled at them both a little ashamedly and began to play a Strauss waltz which had been one of her teacher's favourite pieces as well as her own, gradually forgetting her audience as the music took over. This time when she finished Richard looked approving.

'That was better. Very nice, in fact. What you lack in technique you make up for in feeling. Do you know any Chopin?'

Sharon shook her head, then said boldly, 'But I'd love to hear you play some. Lee tells me you're the musician in the family.'

'No longer to be alone, it seems.' He lifted his shoulders in good-humoured resignation as she slid invitingly from the stool. 'All right, but I'm very much out of practice.'

Lee moved a hand as she turned to find a seat, patting the arm of his chair in a gesture half invitation, half command. His arm came behind her when she obeyed the summons, his hand resting lightly against her outer thigh, his shoulder touching the side of her breast as she put her own arm along the back of the chair to support herself. She was vitally aware of that contact the whole time his father was playing, feeling the warmth of his fingers penetrating the material of her skirt.

Sitting there that way in the warm intimacy of the room with music filling her ears, she looked ahead to a future which glowed golden with promise. It was going to be a good marriage, she told herself with certainty, despite its unconventional start. She would make Lee a wife to be proud of!

CHAPTER THREE

STANDING beside her husband to greet the wedding guests a month later, Sharon could still scarcely persuade herself it was all really over. She had to keep touching the rings on her finger to bring conviction.

These last few weeks were ones she would not have cared to go through again. There had been so much to do, so many people to meet; so few moments when she and Lee had been alone together. In so many ways he was still virtually a stranger, she acknowledged now, stealing a glance at the lean features as he smilingly accepted yet another hand in congratulation; a stranger with whom tonight she would share a bed. That particular thought brought a sensation halfway between anticipation and apprehension. He had known other women; might he not find her a disappointment? She suspected that very fear was a good part of the reason why she had not succumbed to his lovemaking on the few occasions when it could have been possible, although she had certainly wanted to do so.

As if sensing her disquiet, Lee seized advantage of a momentary lull in proceedings to give her an encouraging smile. 'Bear up,' he murmured. 'Only a couple of hours, then we can get away.'

Away. Just the two of them. Tonight they would be in Switzerland, free from the curious gaze of all but a skeleton staff in the house at Lake Lucerne. Sharon had not been surprised to learn that the Brents owned other homes, because by then nothing about the whole Brent family would have surprised her very much at all. Secretly she would have preferred to spend her honeymoon somewhere totally new to both of them, but to say so in the face of the offer would have seemed churlish.

Looking down the receiving line, she caught her father-in-law's eye and saw it close in a swift wink. Had it not been for the frosty expression on the face of the woman standing next to him, Sharon would have reciprocated. As it was she could only sigh inwardly and content herself with a smile instead. It would be a long time before Lorna Brent forgave her son for marrying—as she no doubt put it—beneath him, and an even longer one before she accepted her new daughter-in-law as part of the family to which she herself now only belonged by name only. Meeting her for the first time a bare week ago, Sharon had been made instantly aware of antipathy behind the cool greeting. Had arrangements not already been so far ahead, she had the feeling that some private approach might have been made with a view to breaking up the unsuitable romance. In the circumstances there had been little the other could do but show her disapproval in every way possible—a display which had left Lee singularly unmoved.

At least his sister Lora appeared to bear no ill will. Her chief reaction on seeing her brother for the first time after his engagement had been one of laughing acclamation. 'You did it!' she said. 'You really went and did it!' He hadn't then, but he certainly had now. Husband and wife—Mr and Mrs Lee Brent. It still seemed unreal.

As the only bridesmaid, Maureen was having a whale of a time flirting with the best man, who was taking it very much in his stride. Sharon could count on one hand the number of people who were here on her personal invitation, and they did not include her aunt and uncle. True, there had been a present from them both, and a telegram this morning, but Aunt Dorothy had made it clear from the first that they would not be coming down because Uncle Brian couldn't get the time off from work. In consequence, it had been a near-stranger who had walked her down the aisle and given her away, and Sharon was keenly aware that everyone had known it. But that was behind her now, and more important matters lay ahead.

She went up to change ahead of Lee, accompanied by Maureen. Viewing the bedroom which was to be theirs on their return three weeks hence, she tried to imagine what it would be like to live in this beautiful house on a permanent basis. One thing was certain, she would have to take over some of the running of it herself. Having a full-time housekeeper might be all right for some, but what did it leave the mistress of the house to do with her time? She wished it were possible to dispense with Mrs Reynolds altogether, but they could hardly ask the woman to leave without good reason.

Maureen had gone to the window to look out over the gardens, drawing in deep breaths of the spring-scented air.

'It's a dream world,' she said, echoing Sharon's own thoughts on the subject. 'You must have been born lucky!' She turned then, her generous nature reasserting itself. 'No, I didn't mean that. It takes more than just luck to have a man like Lee fall in love with you. I hope you'll be ecstatically happy, Sharon.'

'Thanks.' There was a lump in Sharon's throat. Impulsively she added, 'We mustn't lose touch just because I'll be living out here. You must come and visit, and we'll meet when I get up to town. Lee's keeping on the apartment to use when we want to see a show or spend an evening out.' She laughed then, and shook her head. 'You're right, it is a dream world. I still keep thinking I'm going to waken up any minute!'

The other girl became suddenly practical. 'You'd better start getting changed before your husband comes up and finds us wasting time chatting. You're due to leave for the airport in about forty minutes.'

'Yes.' The thought of Lee walking into the room before she was ready somehow unnerved her, although no doubt that was something she would become accustomed to. She said swiftly, 'You go on down, Maureen, I can manage. Anyway, you have to be ready to catch the bouquet when I throw it from the stairs.'

'I've had my elbows specially sharpened.' Smiling, she walked to the door. 'See you in a little while.'

Left alone, Sharon gathered together her going-away outfit and took it through with her to the bathroom, locking the door behind her with a faint sense of ridiculousness. Lee would no doubt agree with her: she was being silly, and she would certainly have to get over it, but not right now when it was all so new. They had three weeks to become at ease with one another, three weeks of being alone together, seeking company only if they felt like it. For her part, Sharon was sure she would not feel like it. She wanted to be with Lee and only with Lee.

The bathroom window was open and she could hear someone talking on the side section of terrace immediately below, voices surprisingly clear and carrying:

'Oh, she's quite a pretty little thing, I'll grant you, and not unintelligent, but she isn't ... well, you know what I mean. I never thought Lee would really go and do it.'

'You mean you knew he was seeing her before he

dropped this on you?' asked another feminine voice, and Lora laughed.

'Seeing is hardly the word! Giving him an ultimatum like that was the worst thing Daddy could have done! Of course, you didn't know about that, did you?' She paused, tone changing a little. 'Entirely between the two of us, you realise?'

'Well, naturally.' There was curiosity in the other voice. 'It all sounds terribly mysterious!'

'Not really. About par for the course when you know my brother as well as I do. Actually, I'm not supposed to be in the know myself. I just happened to overhear Daddy tell Lee that if he wasn't prepared to find himself a wife and settle down, the presidency would go to cousin Ronald instead when he retires in September. That was a couple of months ago. Not long before my own wedding, as a matter of fact. Anyway, Lee said if a wife was the only requirement he'd go out and pick himself one up off the streets. That's exactly what he did too—she told me herself. He asked her to marry him a week later.'

'And she snatched at the chance!'

'Well, wouldn't you, darling, in her position? Though I say it myself, that brother of mine is a catch by any standards. Luckily Daddy likes her, so he's prepared to overlook any shortcomings. He's given the two of them White Ladies as a wedding present. More than Jason and I got from him, I can tell you—but Lee always was his favourite.'

There was an audible sniff. 'I can't understand him. If he had to get married at all why not choose a wife who'd be a help to him, not a hindrance?'

Lora laughed. 'Someone like you, for instance?'

'Well, at least we move in the same circles!'

'Ah, yes, darling, but with you he wouldn't have quite

the same freedom to please himself, would he? You'd be wanting to know where he'd been and who with every time he elected to stay out overnight.'

'And you think she won't?'

'I doubt it. I shouldn't think she has the nerve to question his movements in any way. Lee will have covered that aspect, don't worry. A great manipulator of angles, is my bother.'

Sharon heard no more because she stopped listening at that point. It would have been better, she thought numbly, had she never listened in the first place. Her whole body felt bruised. Picked up off the streets—could any phrase be more explicit? There was no doubt in her mind that what she had heard was the simple truth. It explained away too many things. Lee had married her, not because he loved her, but in answer to a challenge thrown out by his father. She was his retaliation, his means of conforming to requirements while also rejecting them.

Turning, she caught sight of her reflection in the full-length mirror. The bride wore white, she reflected in pain. For virginity substitute stupidity, for stupid was what she had been in not realising before this that Lee didn't love her. Want her, yes—on the strength of past close encounters she was willing to go along with that particular aspect of his involvement. But desire was an emotion any man could feel for any woman—and in Lee's case one he had obviously indulged to the full. In love or not, tonight he would expect to make love to her, and look for her response. If she asked herself what she could do about it, there was only one answer: she had to go through with it. It was too late to back out.

Anger swept suddenly through her, swamping the pain. Was it, though? Was that really all the pride she had in herself? It might be too late to back out of the marriage itself without invoking a great deal of trouble, but there was no law which could force her to accept her position in Lee's scheme of things. He had married her in response to an ultimatum, so why not issue one of her own? If she stayed with him it would be on her terms, not his!

The knock on the door startled her. 'Are you almost through, Sharon?' asked Lee from the bedroom. 'We have about fifteen minutes before we leave.'

From somewhere Sharon found the control to answer, surprised by the steadiness of her voice as she did so. 'Just a few minutes.'

She took a last look at the girl in the white dress before she took it off, seeing the darkened blue eyes harden into resolve. She would show them. She would show them all! No one was ever going to hurt her like this again.

Lee was already changed into a dark fawn suit when she eventually joined him. He eyed her own choice of tan and cream dress and plain toning coat with approval. 'We blend,' he said softly, and paused studying her. 'You look ... different.'

'Fine feathers,' she returned. 'Wasn't that what you intended when you gave me that cheque last week?'

'The one you were so reluctant to accept?' He shook his head, smiling a little. 'It was simply the first instalment of a regular monthly allowance, that's all.'

'Presented early to enable me to kit myself out with a trousseau fitted for my new station in life.' She said it lightly. 'I'm not complaining. I really enjoyed spending it once I got used to the idea of not having to count the cost.'

'Good.' There was a faint line between his brows. Watching him, Sharon could almost hear him deciding to attribute her brittleness to nerves. He made no attempt to come near her. 'We'd better go,' he said. 'The car will be waiting. Don't forget your bouquet—the girls would never forgive you.'

'Ah yes, tradition!' She took it up from the chair where Maureen had carefully placed it in readiness for this very moment not half an hour ago, looking at the delicate arrangement of spring flowers which only that morning had seemed to symbolise just what was in her heart without any feeling whatsoever. 'Let's get it over with.'

A cheer went up from the throng of people gathered in the wide hallway as the two of them appeared at the head of the stairs. Sharon paused on the curve, eyes searching the upturned faces for Maureen's familiar one, hand drawing back to toss the bouquet the moment she found what she sought. But it wasn't Maureen who caught it. Someone taller standing behind her thrust forward a hand and scooped it out of the air before her reaching fingers could touch it, holding it aloft with a smile of derisive triumph. Meeting the other eyes, Sharon had the sudden curious certainty that this was the woman Lora had been speaking to down on the terrace not long ago, yet she felt nothing. She was safe inside her shell— inviolate. She intended to stay that way.

The following moments were hectic. Lee leaned back in his seat with a sigh of relief when the car at last moved off down the drive.

'Thank God that's over,' he said with feeling. 'I'd hate to think I'd to face it over again!' He glanced her way, the smile in his eyes as well as on his lips. 'If you ever decide to divorce me, I'll stay single for the rest of my life!'

Mockery, Sharon thought. It would never occur to him to believe her capable of such an act. One way or another, he was in for quite a few surprises.

'I shan't divorce you,' she said. 'What grounds would I have?'

'None at all.' He leaned over and kissed her, heedless of the chauffeur's presence beyond the sliding glass screen. 'We'll be at the house in time for late dinner. Lucerne is beautiful at this time of the year.'

'I'm sure it is.' She made no move to draw away from him. 'I'm looking forward to seeing it.'

'And I to showing it to you.' His tone deepened. 'Among other things.'

That, Sharon told herself cynically, she could believe. Too bad he was going to be denied even that much compensation.

They reached the house at Lucerne in darkness after an uneventful journey. It was some distance from the town itself, nestling among the trees which grew right down to the water's edge at that point. Sharon had a vague impression of timbered gables and solid strength before she was whisked inside to a great living hall which rose clear to the rafters. A stone fireplace at one end held what seemed on the face of it a totally unnecessary pyre of crackling logs, although there was no denying the air of welcome they imparted.

The middle-aged couple who greeted them, Sharon already knew, were the caretaker and his wife who would be looking after them during the coming three weeks. Their English, she discovered without surprise, was a great deal better than her scanty French. Lee introduced them as Henri and Suzette Delon. They had been with the family for fifteen years, and would no doubt stay until their eventual retirement.

Soft gold window drapes were already drawn in the room they were to share, hanging in silken folds across the whole breadth of one cedar-clad wall. There was thick, cream-coloured carpet beneath her feet, and twin double beds draped in the same heavy silk which covered the windows. Here again was a wide stone fireplace, but though ready laid the fire itself remained unlit.

Suzette took Sharon through to show her the adjoining bathroom while Henri fetched up their luggage. It was huge and beautifully fitted, containing a separate shower cabinet in addition to the one positioned over the low bath. Thick brown and gold towels nestled invitingly over the rails.

'This was the Master and Mistress's suite when they would come here together,' the Frenchwoman said. 'Now it is one of the smaller rooms the Master uses instead.' Her tone was momentarily saddened. 'It is good for it to be in use again. Always I have tried to keep it just so.'

'You've kept it beautifully,' Sharon assured her, and felt the warmth fade from her as Lee appeared in the doorway.

'We'll be ready to eat in twenty minutes or so, Suzette,' he said pleasantly in French.

'*Oui, monsieur.*' She gave a beaming smile which encompassed them both, and went out past him.

Lee remained where he was, tilting his head quizzically as he looked across at Sharon. 'Like it?'

'So far,' she agreed coolly. She knew that if she went to pass him in order to return to the bedroom he was going to take hold of her, yet she could hardly stand around in here all night either. 'Only a fool could find anything to dislike about a place like this.'

As she had anticipated, he caught her by the shoulders as she reached him, turning her to face him, expression a little uncertain. 'Sharon, what is it? Something bothering you?'

'Apart from being tired and hungry, do you mean?' she asked. 'That was my first flight, Lee. I'm not . . . adjusted yet.'

'Of course.' He dropped a light kiss on her forehead.

'It's been a tiring day. Things will seem better after we've both relaxed for an hour or so over a good meal. Why don't you put on something comfortable? I can change later.'

Sharon didn't argue with the suggestion. She wanted badly to be alone for a few minutes. None of what was to come was going to be easy, but there was no slackening in her resolve. This marriage was a travesty to which she had no intention of contributing further. That she bore the Brent name at all was more than enough.

With Lee gone, she opened the suitcase and found a floor-length caftan in heavy white cotton edged about the high neckline and long flowing sleeves with narrow gold braid. Sliding into it after a quick shower, she didn't even bother to glance at her reflection in the long mirrors fronting the concealed wardrobe, leaving her face free of make-up and simply smoothing a hand over her hair. She felt detached—almost as if she viewed herself from a distance. This was her wedding night and it meant nothing to her, other than something to be got through.

Lee was waiting for her downstairs, sitting on a long, padded settee at right angles to the fire. He had taken off his suit jacket and his tie, and loosened the top two buttons of his shirt. Looking down on the crisp dark head from the gallery above, Sharon stifled a momentary pang for what might have been. That way lay pain and heartache, and she wanted neither. What she did want was a simple understanding between them, and that was what she was going to have.

Dinner was served in a corner of the long, covered veranda room at the rear of the house, the table beautifully set for two with silver candelabrum creating a soft intimacy. The windows were floor length and sliding, opening on to another section of the veranda which actually overhung the moon-silvered water. Underneath, Lee said, was the boathouse and workshop.

'We'll run up to the town in the morning, if you like,' he suggested. 'The main tourist season is only just getting under way, so it shouldn't be too busy. We can have coffee with Jacques Cabot, a friend who owns one of the waterfront hotels. You'll like Jacques.' He smiled. 'And he'll adore you! Blondes are his one acknowledged weakness.'

'I'm not blonde,' Sharon denied. 'Not strictly. I could always have it lightened, of course.'

'No way.' He said it with emphasis. 'I like it the way it is.' He studied her across the table, his expression altering. 'I wonder if I was very selfish bringing you here. We don't have to stay the whole three weeks. We could go down to Marseille and take the yacht along the coast. She isn't under charter till next month.'

'How big is it?' Sharon asked, momentarily distracted.

'Eighty feet—not enormous by Riviera standards, but she can cruise eight people in comfort. She's normally chartered June, July and August. The rest of the year the crew is on stand-by. Are you a good sailor?'

'I'm not sure,' she said. 'The farthest I've been is across the Channel and it was always fairly calm.'

'You've visited France several times before then?'

'Only Brittany. My uncle and aunt have a caravan. They use it on their annual holiday. I went with them until I was seventeen.'

'Always to the same place?'

'Yes.' There was a challenge in her glance. 'They like it, and people know them now.'

His shrug was easy. 'Each to their own. There was no criticism to defend them against, Sharon. Even if there had been why should you care? They couldn't take the trouble to come and see you married.'

'Uncle Brian couldn't get the time off.'

'That's nonsense, and you know it.'

'All right.' She wasn't prepared to argue about it. It didn't matter anyway. Nothing mattered outside of the knowledge which burned at the back of her mind. She switched back to the original question, choosing her words with deliberation. 'It doesn't really make any difference whether we go or stay, the situation will be the same.'

His eyes narrowed a little at her tone. 'I'm not sure I follow you.'

'I mean I'll still be the wife you picked up off the streets.'

'What the devil are you talking about?'

His curtness left her strangely unmoved. 'Do you deny ever using that phrase?'

'Of course I damned well ...' He stopped, expression undergoing an abrupt change. 'My father told you that?'

'No, he didn't.'

'Then how ...'

'Let's say you were overheard.'

'Lora!' The name came out like an explosion. 'It's just about typical of her!'

'She seems to have the same high opinion of your code of ethics,' Sharon remarked on the same unemotional note. 'Par for the course was how she put it. Apparently the two of you know one another pretty well.'

'She doesn't know me at all. Not now. We haven't lived in the same house for ten years.' He paused, the anger giving way to something else. 'Sharon, it wasn't the way you think. I was being pressured and I said it off the top. You don't really imagine I knocked you down that day for the express purpose of getting you to marry me, do you?'

The irony penetrated deep enough to strengthen her

resolve. 'No,' she said. 'I think that idea came later when you realised that if you had to marry at all you'd be better off with a little nobody like me who'd be so overwhelmed by her own good fortune she'd never dream of questioning anything you did—or continued to do. Perhaps it was a way of getting back at your father too. After all, he must have had his own idea of the kind of wife his only son should take.'

'You're right, he did. Someone who'd stabilise my way of life was what I think he had in mind.' He hadn't moved from his seat; the candlelight played across the planes and angles of his face, hardening the jawline. 'Just when did Lora tell you all this?'

'She didn't. I overheard *her* talking to someone else on the terrace when I was changing. She made it very plain that she shared your mother's opinion of my suitability as a wife for you.'

Lee made a sudden emphatic gesture. 'I'm not going to spend the night apologising for my mother and sister. What I said was said before we met.'

'I know.' Her own voice was low. 'It was also you who said that fate steps in at the most surprising moments.'

'Which you're twisting to meet your own interpretation.' He put out his hand towards her. 'Sharon . . .'

'No!' She was on her feet before he could touch her, trembling a little but still in control. 'I won't listen!'

His fingers closed about her wrist as she reached the door, bringing her to a halt with a jerk.

'If you go anywhere you go with me,' he said harshly. 'We're going to talk this thing through if we have to sit up all night doing it!'

Neither Suzette nor her husband appeared to be around as they crossed the hall to reach the staircase, much to Sharon's relief. Lee's grip was like iron on her wrist, his features grimly set. She steeled herself for what was to come.

One of the Delons had been up and put a light to the fire while they had been eating. Lee put her into a chair close to it and stood for a moment looking down at her with an expression she found hard to decipher.

'Why wait till now to bring this up?' he asked at length on a hard note. 'As you so obviously decided my motives the moment you heard Lora's little piece, why not come out with it there and then?'

Her shrug was defensive. 'I had to have time to think —to decide what I was going to do.'

'And what exactly did you decide?'

She made herself meet his eyes unflinchingly. 'I'll stay with you, Lee, but that's all. I don't want you ... touching me.'

'I see.' It was difficult to assess his reaction. 'And supposing I'm not prepared to accept that state of affairs?'

'You'll have to, if you want the presidency.' Her voice sounded thick. 'If stability is what your father is looking for, then I hardly think he'd be favourably impressed if our marriage ended within the space of a few hours.'

'You're threatening to walk out on me now, tonight, if I don't agree?'

'Yes.'

'You wouldn't get very far.'

'I'd manage.'

His whole face tightened, abruptly, teeth coming together with an audible sound. 'You little fool, I ought to slap some sense into you!' He reached down and jerked her to her feet, holding her there in front of him with fingers clamped about her upper arms just above the elbow. 'You're not walking out on me in any sense, Sharon. I won't let you!'

'A few hours or a few days, it isn't going to make much difference in the long run.' Her voice levelled. 'I mean it, Lee. Either leave me alone or I'll make sure your father knows just what lengths you're capable of!'

He stared at her for what seemed an age before he spoke again, obviously shaken by the determination in her. 'I'm just beginning to realise what really lies behind this decision of yours,' he said at last. 'You got everything you wanted out of this marriage the moment you acquired the name, didn't you? It never was me, just what I represented.'

'If you like.' She was beyond denying anything. 'Although I'd have forced myself to go through with the rest of it if I hadn't . . .'

'If you hadn't found what seemed like the perfect excuse for having your cake without having to pay for it,' he finished for her. The grey eyes held an unholy light. 'Unfortunately, it isn't going to be quite as easy as that. You'll pay for it, all right!'

Sharon tried to avoid his mouth as he pulled her to him. 'I told you!' she cried.

'I know what you told me, and I don't give a damn!' he came back savagely. 'You wanted the name, you'll take what goes with it!'

The kiss was brutal, a ravishment all on its own. She felt his hands slide under her to bring her up against him, holding her relentlessly until she stopped struggling, then moulding her in a caress which brought sudden fire racing through her veins. The muscles of his thighs were hard and unyielding, forcing hers to yield to them. In spite of everything she could feel the desire rising in her, turning her spine to water and bringing the blood drumming into her ears. When he released her with a sudden, bitten-off sound of disgust it was almost a disappointment.

'To hell with it!' he said. 'Do as you like!'

He turned from her and went into the bathroom, slamming the door behind him. Sharon stared after him, desperately trying to bring herself under control. If he had carried on she would have been beyond stopping him—beyond even wanting to stop him.

So what happens now? she wondered painfully. She hadn't considered beyond the point of confrontation at all. She sat down again in the chair behind her, fighting the urge to burst into tears. It was too late for that. If she was going to see this thing through at all it had to be with fortitude and a hardened heart. Do as you like, Lee had said. But what? She wished she knew.

It was some time before the bathroom door opened again. Lee stood framed for a moment looking across at her, face controlled.

'Like it or not,' he said, 'we're going to have to talk.'

'About what?' Her voice was husky.

'About where we go from here.' The pause was brief. 'That offer you made me to stay on if I leave you alone—I accept.'

Her head jerked. 'You ... do?'

'What did you expect? We'll both be gaining our main objective.' He was openly sneering. 'My father believes you're capable of learning all you need to know to become an asset to the business. I think you are too—especially in the light of the performance you've been putting on these last few weeks. You realise we're both going to have to be pretty convincing where my father is concerned?'

Now that it was all over, Sharon wanted suddenly to go back, to start over again and try finding some other solution. Ever since she had learned what she had from Lora's outspoken comments, she had been travelling in an emotional no-man's-land, not thinking ahead of the moment when she would accuse Lee. If she had kept her mouth shut the basic facts would have remained unchanged, but she would have stood at least a chance of having him come to feel something deeper for her one day. Now there was no chance at all; she had taken care of that too effectively. There was a new coldness about the grey eyes, a harder line to his mouth than she had ever seen there before. He was convinced that she had only married him for material gain, and that was something he would not be prepared to forgive and forget, regardless of anything else.

'Yes,' she said, 'I realise that. Don't worry, I shan't let you down.'

'Then we have a bargain. You can have all the things you want, and I'll keep my freedom.'

'Did you ever really consider giving it up?'

His glance ran over her very slowly and very deliberately. 'You might have provided enough distraction for a time. I hadn't considered further than that. It's hardly relevant now, is it?' He came away from the door-jamb, the movement abrupt. 'We'd better get to bed.'

Sharon sat up further in the chair, eyes darkening. 'You're not sleeping in here?'

'Where else? We're supposed to be on honeymoon, remember?'

'I don't care. If you insist on staying in this room, I'll have another on my own.'

'No, you won't.' There was an inflexible look to his jawline. 'Things like that have a way of getting round. We'll share a room here, and we'll share back at White Ladies.' He took off his shirt and slung it over the end of the nearest bed before walking up to the head to reach under a pillow and extract a folded pair of blue silk pyjamas. 'I'll have that shower now, then the bathroom's all yours.'

Sharon waited until she heard the water running before getting stiffly to her feet. Only now, on looking round, did she realise that all the unpacking had been done and the suitcases removed. Suzette had laid out her own choice of nightdress for her new mistress across the other turned-down bed, a froth of transparent white nylon falling from tiny shoulder straps which Sharon herself had bought with her wedding night in view. She seized it up now in hasty hands and thrust it out of sight in a drawer, taking out a cool cotton voile with a matching peignoir from one of the fitted wardrobes.

Her throat ached with a tight, dry pain which made it difficult to swallow. Had things been different she would have been in Lee's arms, feeling his hard, lean body close to her, the touch of his lips; hearing his voice murmuring soft words. Love of a kind, if not the kind she had imagined, but she had thrown that away too.

Lee emerged barefooted but wearing the blue silk pyjamas a few moments later. He didn't glance in her direction, but went across to his bed and slid between the sheets to lie with his head resting on his raised arms looking at the ceiling. Sharon took her things into the bathroom and closed the door quietly between them.

All her toilet articles were neatly set out on the long marble shelf next to Lee's, her talcum powder rubbing shoulders with his aftershave. She took her time cleansing and moisturising her face, and an even longer time brushing first teeth and then hair. Eventually she could stave off the moment of return to the other room no longer. She pulled the peignoir more securely about her as she opened the door.

Lee was lying on his side now, she saw, head turned away from the other bed. From the evenness of his breathing he appeared to be asleep. That was as much as it had all meant to him. A ruined wedding night, and he could sleep! Yet why not? she thought bitterly. It would hardly have been a novel experience for him!

The log in the fireplace had burned to a faint red glow, leaving behind the odour of pine. Sharon got into bed and switched out the light incorporated into the console on her left, then lay there in the darkness listening to sounds of a house settling for the night. It was hours before she slept.

CHAPTER FOUR

SHE awoke facing an empty bed and a window streaming sunlight through partially drawn curtains. Recollection came slowly but inexorably. Sharon rolled on to her back with a deep sigh, wondering how she was going to face the situation ahead of her.

Her bedside clock said nine-thirty. Throwing back the covers with a sudden decisive gesture, she got up and slid her feet into the velvet mules, then padded across to the window to draw back the curtains a little further. There was a glazed door leading on to the balcony beyond. She went out into warm sunshine, her spirits lifting a little at the view.

In front of her the water stretched bright and sparkling to the wooded lower slopes of a mountain range still white-capped beneath a cloudless blue sky. A lake steamer moved slowly along the middle distance, with a couple of smaller craft between it and the shore, perfectly positioned to lend balance to the picture. Sharon drew in a breath of invigorating air and decided that nothing could be so bad on a day like this.

One of the smaller boats was making its way shorewards, and she watched it for some minutes before realising that the man in it was Lee. Despite the distance between them, she turned and went back inside. When she faced him again she wanted to be prepared, both physically and mentally.

It took her only a few minutes to shower and dress in a sleeveless white linen. Her face in the mirror looked pale. She would have to acquire a tan while she was here, she thought, and felt a shudder run through her. Three weeks. How would they get through them? Could two people share the intimacy of sleeping in the same room, eating at the same table, being together every day and still remain aloof? She didn't know because she had never tried it before. Neither, she was sure, had Lee. When it came to the test, it seemed very likely that his will was going to prove stronger than hers, because for him emotion did not enter into it. She only wished she could shut off her own in the same way.

Suzette was dusting in the hall when she finally ventured downstairs, the feathers whisking briskly from surface to surface. She paused when she saw Sharon, an arch little smile on her lips.

'Madame slept well?' she enquired. 'Monsieur Brent said for you not to be disturbed. He has taken out the boat.'

'Yes, I know. I saw him from the balcony.' Sharon hesitated, not sure enough of herself to ask for food at this hour.

'You would like breakfast now?' asked the other, relieving her of the problem.

'Only coffee and toast,' she said gratefully. 'Thank you. I'm sorry to interrupt your routine.'

A look of surprise crossed the Frenchwoman's features. 'It is no trouble *madame*. You would like it brought outside?'

'Yes, please.' There was faint colour in Sharon's cheeks. She must learn to speak and act like the mistress of the house as was expected of her, and not some gauche schoolgirl—especially if she planned to usurp a little of Mrs Reynolds' authority when they got back to White Ladies. Even more now, she was going to need something to occupy her mind, and she doubted very much whether Lee would countenance her taking a job. What was it he had said last night? Something about her learning to become an asset to the business. She wasn't sure what that meant exactly. Entertaining, perhaps. Acting hostess at business dinner parties? The very thought was daunting.

Catching a glimpse of herself in a mirror as she moved towards the door, she reflected disparagingly that she didn't even look the part she was expected to play. Pretty, Lora had called her; insipid was what she had probably meant. There was no sparkle, no glamour; she lacked sophistication. No wonder Lee hadn't been unduly moved by the loss of her company in his bed last night. The women he was accustomed to were more like his sister: poised and confident; beautifully dressed. The one she had on now had cost the earth, yet it didn't look right on her because she was all wrong.

Lee was coming up the steps from the boathouse when she got outside on the veranda. He was wearing dark blue shorts and a matching tee-shirt, his legs and arms still bearing a tan beneath their light coating of hair. He had been here in Switzerland skiing in February, she remembered him telling her a few days ago, and she knew he played squash at least three times a week when he was home in London. He looked every inch the sports-man, lithe and muscular.

The sun glasses he had on effectively concealed his expression as he moved towards her. Sharon controlled the urge to back away from him.

'Suzette is bringing me out some coffee,' she said diffidently. 'Shall I tell her you're here?'

'She'll see I'm here when she comes,' he returned. 'If the pot isn't large enough she can always bring more.' He pulled out a chair from the round table with its bright yellow cloth, and sat down, eyeing her with lifted brow when she remained standing. 'Not staying?'

She seated herself abruptly in the opposite chair, leaning her forearm along the rail at her side to gaze out over the sun-kissed water. 'Did you enjoy your sail?'

'Yes.' His tone was clipped. 'We can dispense with the small-talk when there's no one else around.'

Her eyes came back to him, drawn against her will. 'Can't we at least be ... friendly?'

'The word is civilised.'

'All right then, civilised.' She tried to sound calm and level about it. 'After all, if we're going to be here together for three weeks, we can't spend the whole time in silence.'

'We're not going to be here three weeks,' he said. 'Another couple of days, then we leave for Marseille.' His lips twisted. 'We'll have the crew for company, plus friends in every port. You'll enjoy the *Ventura*, she's quite a boat.'

'I'm sure she is.' Sharon swallowed on the lump in her throat. 'Do we have to go?'

The answer was uncompromising. 'Yes. Last night I came to the conclusion that there was little point in prolonging a meaningless honeymoon, yet going home early was no solution either. The yacht was the best I could think of. You can pick up any extra clothes you might need in Marseille.'

The arrival of Suzette with the coffee and hot toast forestalled any reply. Not that there was much Sharon could say. She wanted neither to go to the yacht nor to stay on here, yet as Lee had pointed out, to cut short their honeymoon could only lead to awkward questions. They had to stay away the whole three weeks.

'What do we do for the next couple of days?' she asked when Suzette had departed.

He shrugged. 'You haven't seen anything of Lucerne yet. And there's Jacques to meet.'

Her head came up sharply. 'That's hardly necessary now, is it? Why look for difficulties?'

'Because he'll expect to be introduced to my wife and feel slighted if he isn't. He's too old a friend to be treated that way.'

She tried another tack. 'If he's so old a friend, mightn't he guess things aren't as they should be between us?'

'It's up to the two of us to make sure he doesn't. As a Frenchman, he's likely to be pretty observant when it comes to emotional relationships, so it won't be easy to deceive him about ours.'

'Then why bother trying? Does it matter so much what he thinks?'

The dark glasses concealed the expression in his eyes, but the compression about his mouth told its own story.

'Yes, it matters.'

'Male pride?' she sneered, ignoring the warning signals in her need to get at him in some way. 'You don't want your old friend to know you were married for your money?'

This time there was no doubting that she had scored a hit. She saw one hand clench over the arm end of his chair until the knuckles showed white. Regret sheared through her, bringing words stumbling to her lips. 'Lee, I didn't mean that.'

'You meant it.' His tone was flat. 'And you're quite right, I don't want Jacques to know that. I'll make it worth your while to convince him otherwise.'

Sharon flushed hotly. 'That's a horrible thing to say!'

'Why? You were prepared to sell your body for material gain initially. All I'm asking is a fair return for payment rendered.'

'Or you'll put me back on the streets where I came from?'

'Your words, not mine.' Her sarcasm left him unmoved. 'You're safe enough from that, and you know it. You gained the whip hand in deducing the way my father is likely to react if my marriage breaks up so soon. On the other hand, come September when he delegates control of the Company, you might find yourself out of a job if you haven't played your cards right in the meantime.'

She stared at him, trying to find some chink in the armour. 'And if I do?' she said at last, voice low.

'Then we'll see. At least while I'm married to you I have a valid reason for not marrying anyone else.' He finished his coffee and pushed back his chair. 'I'm going to change. Be ready to leave in half an hour. We'll take the launch.'

Left alone, Sharon looked down at her hand clutching the untasted cup of coffee, biting her lip until the pain grew too much. If she hadn't said enough last night to convince Lee of her true colours, she had certainly done so this morning. When would she learn to think ahead before she opened her mouth? Nothing was ever going to persuade him that what she had said had been said just to hurt and not because it was the truth.

Yet was it so far from the truth? some hitherto silent

little voice asked in her mind. Would she have felt quite the same way over Lee if he'd been an ordinary nine-to-fiver with a normal income and way of life? From the first moment of their meeting she had been aware of him as a man of financial status. Could that knowledge have influenced the speed with which her feelings for him had developed? It certainly hadn't taken long, had it? One week to fall in love. If she really loved him so deeply she would have ignored his sister's chatty confidences—or at least given him the opportunity to speak for himself before hitting back. She was attracted to him physically, there was no doubt, but beyond that she was suddenly uncertain.

She shut off that particular line of self-questioning and straightened her shoulders. It hardly mattered either way now. She had two choices: she could retain her position as Lee's wife in name only, as they had agreed last night, or she could leave him and return to her former life. Except that it wasn't that easy, was it? Divorces took time, even when the grounds were valid. And what were her grounds, anyway? Most people would consider her a very fortunate young woman. Lee hadn't abused her; he hadn't considered her worth the effort.

Annulment, then. She stopped there, knowing she couldn't go through with it. There was only one choice when it all boiled down: She did as Lee wanted and acted the part of his loving wife to the best of her ability. And she started today with this Jacques person.

In any other circumstances, Sharon would have loved every minute of the journey up the lake to the town on its north-west point. The boat was sleek and fast, cutting across the surface of the water like a silver dart. They passed close by one of the lake steamers carrying a sizeable complement of passengers, including what appeared to be a party of schoolchildren who all waved enthusiastically.

'Probably English,' said Lee, lifting a hand in his turn. 'They usually come early to take advantage of lower prices. They could even be staying at Jacques' place. He said he was expecting a school party last week when I phoned through.'

'How long have you known him?' Sharon asked as they came round in a wide half turn towards the landing stage jutting out below the big, green-roofed building which was their destination.

'Since we were boys. He inherited this place from his father.' He cut the engine to bring them skilfully alongside, tossing a painter to a youth already standing there waiting to receive it.

There were people sitting at tables on the sun deck above, waiters flitting among them bearing coffee and other refreshments. From what Sharon could hear in passing, the main language being spoken was French, although she thought she caught a couple of words in English from one table.

Lee attracted a great deal of attention from a party of girls in their early twenties seated towards the rear of the deck. Sharon almost envied them their complete lack of self-consciousness as they made audible, laughing remarks which brought a fleeting smile to Lee's lips. They were all three attractive enough to get away with anything, and they knew it. Lee thought so too, judging from the comprehensive glance he swept over them in passing.

Jacques Cabot came out to them in the lobby. He was small and dark, with a pair of very blue, humorously twinkling eyes in a thin brown face: French to his finger-tips, especially in his manner of greeting Sharon. He made her feel special—almost beautiful—holding her hand in his with warm ardour in his gaze.

'The English rose,' he said. 'Such skin! You're a lucky man, Lee!'

'Aren't I?' The irony was only faintly discernible.

They had coffee in the small private sitting room which formed part of a self-contained flat on the ground floor. Jacques sat beside Sharon on the sofa, his whole attention flatteringly concentrated on drawing her out. She had heard enough about the French male to realise that this was probably how he treated all women on principle, yet it failed to detract from the moment. He was taking the trouble, and that was what mattered.

'So you're going to Marseille,' he remarked at one point. 'Does Switzerland interest you so little that you spend only a few days here?'

'It's Lee's choice,' she defended, avoiding the grey eyes opposite. 'He wants to go sailing.'

'On your honeymoon?' with a sad shake of the head in the other man's direction. 'Shame on you, my friend!'

'The crew will be doing the work,' came the unabashed retort, accompanied by a smile which failed to reach his eyes. 'She'll be under charter from next month, and Sharon has never visited the Riviera before.'

'Then I almost wish I was coming with you,' turning back to her with a wicked sparkle. 'To see it all through fresh eyes—show you places even this husband of yours doesn't know—that would be a wonderful thing!'

'Another time maybe,' Lee said dryly. 'There are limits to friendship. Why don't you find yourself a wife, Jacques, and have your own honeymoon?'

'Because all the best ones are already taken,' with a heartfelt sigh and a lingering glance at Sharon's faintly flushed cheeks and reddened lips. 'If we'd met before Lee found you ... who knows what might have happened!'

Her smile was without restraint for the first time in many hours. 'You can say that knowing you're safe anyway.'

'Such modesty!' He shook his head chidingly. 'You do me an injustice. You can apologise by having dinner with me before you leave Lucerne. Your husband too, if absolutely necessary, although he knows I can be trusted with the wife of a friend.'

'I'm sure of it,' responded the friend. 'We'll both be happy to have dinner with you. How about tomorrow?'

Jacques shrugged wry shoulders. 'Another injustice, but I bear no ill will. Tomorrow, then.'

Leaving the hotel for the bright sunlight outside, Lee said sardonically, 'Perhaps I should have let you come alone after all. You obviously find Jacques attractive.'

'I imagine most women do,' Sharon retorted, not about to be drawn. 'He makes an art of being charming, and doesn't expect to be taken seriously.' She paused, glancing at him. 'Do you think it's such a good idea for just the three of us to have dinner together? He's sure to guess something is wrong over a whole evening.'

'There's no reason why he should guess anything unless we underline it for him,' on a brusque note. 'Anyway, it won't be just the three of us. He'll provide another woman for my entertainment so that he can concentrate his attention on you.'

'Why would he do that?'

'Because you intrigue him, and a Frenchman intrigued isn't about to be put off his stroke by minor inconveniences like a husband. Don't look so disbelieving. Wait and see. I've known Jacques a long time, and I doubt if he ever met any girl quite like you before.'

She bridled instantly. 'What's that supposed to mean?'

'What it says. You're different from the general run.'

'No sophistication?' Her tone was hard and bright.

'It's one way of putting it. Not quite the word I'd have chosen myself.'

She refused to give him the satisfaction of asking the obvious, much as she wanted to know the answer. 'I suppose *you'd* find it more natural if I acted like those three at the table back there on the sun deck! You really revelled in that, didn't you?'

'I found it amusing—which was how I was meant to react. They were having themselves a little fun at my expense, that's all.'

'You find those kind of remarks fun?'

He laughed. 'I didn't realise you understood so much French. Why let it worry you? My prowess in bed isn't your concern any more—if it ever was.'

'Perhaps you'd like to make it theirs,' she came back bitingly. 'Go right ahead. They may still be waiting!'

Lee gave her a calculated glance. 'Would you like to continue this conversation in private back at the house?'

Blue eyes met grey for a fleeting instant, and shied away again. Sharon bit her lip. 'No.'

'Then leave it alone, and try to look as if you're enjoying your first sight of the town.'

Sharon did enjoy it because it was impossible not to do so. With its quaint old buildings, its medieval bridges and dreamy atmosphere it was a place which left a lingering impression. Lee took her across the Spreuerbrucke, and the Kapellbrucke spanning the Reuss to look at the paintings under the roofs, the first showing the Totentanz which was a medieval dance of death, the other scenes from Lucerne's past history. Despite it being so early in the season, there were still a lot of people about, and of many nationalities.

They had lunch at the Schwanen where Lee had reserved a table on the small balcony overlooking the lake and mountains, afterwards taking a ride out to Kriens to ascend Mount Pilatus by aerial cableway and view the spectacular panorama laid out before them. There were moments when Sharon could almost forget that any problem existed, but she only had to raise her eyes to Lee's to be reminded. Nothing was going to make him forget easily, that was certain. The knowledge lay like a tangible barrier between them.

Lee was proved right in his prediction. Jacques had invited along another woman to make up a foursome. The latter was an Italian in her mid-twenties, dark-haired and eyed, and voluptuous in her revealing red dress. Her name was Lucia Veldetti. Primed or not, she concentrated all her attention on Lee both during and after the superb meal, leaving Jacques to entertain Sharon, which task he performed with every evidence of pleasure.

They ate in a private room at the hotel, later joining the residents to dance to the music of an excellent combo in the restaurant overlooking the water. It was good promotion, Jacques said laughingly, for the guests to see the owner and his friends enjoying the hotel's own facilities.

As a partner, Sharon found him not so very much taller than herself, yet so wonderfully easy to dance with. He took advantage of the former fact to place his mouth on a level with her ear and whisper the most outrageous things to her as they moved, though always with that hint of laughter which belied any real seriousness.

'Your trouble is you feel you have to live up to the part,' Sharon said, leaning back a little in his arms to shake her head at him in mock remonstration. 'Frenchmen are supposed to be the world's greatest lovers, aren't they?'

He smiled at her wickedly. 'You think it is all talk, eh?'

'I'd be far more impressed if you didn't exaggerate quite as much.'

'In what way do I exaggerate?'

'Every time you open your mouth. I'm not beautiful, and I know it.'

'You don't see yourself through my eyes. Beauty—true beauty—is in the bone structure, not a substance applied with a brush.' His tone was light yet with an underlying note that carried conviction. 'Your hair is pure gold, but the way you wear it blurs the outline. If you were mine, I would put you in the hands of a specialist in such matters and reveal what is there for all the world to admire, not just those with the eyes to see. Did no one else ever tell you you're beautiful?'

He meant Lee, of course. She kept her voice light. 'I've been called pretty.'

'An insipid word. I hadn't thought Lee so lacking in perception.'

As if on cue, the latter came into her line of vision over Jacques' shoulder, head bent towards that of his partner. She couldn't see his face, but from the way he was holding the lusciously curved body in his arms he was finding the going anything but arduous.

'Would you call Lucia beautiful?' she asked without really meaning to.

'In a very different sense. Lucia is a woman men look at with what you would probably call "one thing in mind". She's built for pleasure.'

'Is she your mistress?'

'Not on any permanent arrangement.' He sounded amused. 'We have an understanding, you could say. Are you jealous because Lee pays her attention?'

'Of course not.' The denial was too quick, she saw that from his smile.

'Then you're an even more unusual woman than I thought. Perhaps I should be taken to task for inviting her to join us tonight, but I knew it would take my heaviest ammunition to occupy your husband enough for me to have time alone with you.' He put his lips softly to her cheek, moving them a fraction closer to her mouth with each tiny kiss until she averted her head from him. 'That was cruel,' he murmured sorrowfully. 'So near and yet so far! Just a kiss. What harm can there be in that?'

'Too much,' said Sharon. 'I might enjoy it.'

'I would hope so! Even on honeymoon, an Englishman is so restrained in his emotions—at least in front of others. If I were in Lee's place I'd want the world to know you were mine!'

If he were in Lee's place. She wondered what he would think if he only knew the truth.

Dancing with the man she had married a little later, she found herself comparing the constraint she felt now with the ease she had felt in Jacques' arms. As if able to read her thoughts, Lee deliberately tightened his hold to draw her closer to him.

'Relax,' he said. 'Imagine it's Jacques you're dancing with. You didn't hold yourself away from him.'

'I'm surprised you found time to notice,' she came back. 'Lucia seemed to have your full attention!'

'Physically perhaps.'

'I can imagine!'

'I'm sure you can.'

The inference hurt. She sought for some weapon to use against him. 'Why don't you ask Jacques if you can borrow her for the night?' she suggested on a honeyed note. 'I'm sure he wouldn't mind.'

'An exchange, you mean?' He shook his head, mouth mocking. 'It would hardly be equal.'

It was a moment before she could bring herself to speak again, voice suddenly husky when she did so. 'Must it always be like this? Can't we at least try to talk to one another without fencing all the time?'

Lee shrugged. 'The remedy is in your hands as much as mine.'

'You began it!'

'But you didn't have to continue it.'

She said with heat, 'That's unfair!'

'Probably. Who said anything about being fair? Whatever you get from me, it's only a fraction of what you deserve.'

'Your own motives weren't exactly snow white,' she retorted bitterly, aware of the uselessness in attempting to deny what she herself had made out to be the truth.

'So you tell me.'

'You admitted it.'

'I admitted,' he said, 'to making a rash statement in poor taste some time before I even knew you existed. It could have been a premonition—or an omen.'

Her laugh sounded strained. 'You'll be telling me next that you fell in love with me at first sight!'

'Not quite. I'd say it happened around the time you walked out of the apartment. By the time I'd pulled myself together enough to go after you, you'd vanished.'

She stared at him, the dryness growing in her throat. 'I don't believe you.'

Lee inclined his head. 'It's hardly important any more. The girl I loved never existed outside my imagination. It's reputed to be a particularly blind emotion. One sees what one wants to see.'

'What did you see?' It was barely more than a whisper. She saw the corners of his mouth curl.

'I'm not even sure now. Not that it matters.'

The sense of loss was like a knife twisting inside her.

Lee had loved her; he had really loved her! And she had killed it. Fool that she was, she had thrown away the only thing that gave their relationship any meaning.

She said thickly, 'Oh, God, I wish I knew how to turn the clock back! I've made such a mess of things.'

His eyes were sardonic. 'Who are you trying to impress?'

'I'm not. Not in the way you mean.' She looked at him with desperate pleading, trying to find the words. 'Lee, I was lying when I said I'd married you for money. I wanted to hurt you because I'd been hurt. I was a little fool, and I'm sorry. I know that sounds totally inadequate, but I can't think of any other way of saying it.' Her voice died away before his total lack of response. 'You don't believe me, do you?'

'No,' he said flatly. 'I'm not sure what kind of game you're playing now, but there's no way you're going to turn yourself back into the girl I thought I'd married. We have a business arrangement. Let's keep it that way.'

The music stopped at that point. Without a word, he took her arm to lead her off the floor. Jacques watched the two of them coming with a thoughtful expression on his face, glanced from one to the other as if about to make some comment, then apparently changed his mind.

Lee made no attempt to sit down again. 'I think it's time we were making tracks,' he said. 'It's been a great evening, Jacques. Try and get over later on, if you can. We'd be very glad to have you, wouldn't we, darling?'

Sharon gave a stiff little smile. 'Of course.'

'I'll do my best,' said Jacques. 'No chance of seeing you again before you leave for Marseille?'

'No, we decided to go first thing in the morning instead of waiting another day.' Lee's glance moved to the Italian woman, his mouth taking on a different slant. '*Arrivederci*, Lucia.'

Her smile held a quality of regret. *'Ciao.'*

Jacques accompanied them to the boat, standing by to cast off when they were ready. Tossing the painter aboard, he said cheerfully, 'Make it up before you reach home, eh?'

The roar of the engine made a reply of any kind redundant. Expression giving nothing away, Lee lifted a hand in brief farewell and took them out in a broad sweep to head east down the lake.

Neither spoke during the journey. Sharon felt numb. There seemed no way of getting through to him : nothing she could say that he would believe. When she thought of what might have been but for her mistrust, she wanted to weep.

The Delons had already retired by the time they reached the house. Sharon left Lee making fast the boat and went indoors. In their room she stood for a moment looking across at the two beds, ready turned down for the night. That was their life together, unless she could find some way of persuading him that the girl he had loved still existed. She *had* to find a way.

He was sitting on the edge of his bed when she emerged from the bathroom. His jacket and tie were slung carelessly across the foot, his shirt unbuttoned. Meeting his eyes, Sharon was swept by a wave of emotion. She wanted to run to him, to throw herself into his arms and beg him to love her again, but pride wouldn't allow her to humble herself to quite that depth. She tried another verbal appeal instead, voice unsteady.

'Lee, there has to be something I can say or do that will convince you how I feel.'

He studied her for a long moment, expression unreadable. 'Tell me how you feel,' he said at length.

She swallowed. 'I . . . love you.'

'All right,' he said. 'Come and show me how much.'

He smiled thinly when she failed to move. 'Too shy?'

Sharon forced herself to take the few steps towards him, dropping down in front of him to put her hands over both of his where they rested on his knees and look into his face with every ounce of appeal she could muster.

'I'm telling you the truth,' she said. 'I was wrong to take what Lora said the way I did without at least giving you the chance to explain. I ruined our wedding night, and there's no way I can undo that part of it, but I promise I'll never doubt you again.' She waited, heart sinking further at the coolness in the grey eyes. 'It's no use, is it? You still don't believe me.'

'As a matter of fact, I do,' he returned without inflection. 'I believe you regret ruining what could have been a much better deal than the one you're left with. If you'd carried on the original act you'd have stood to gain much more than you were losing. Besotted husbands can be very generous.'

'Don't,' she begged. 'It wasn't like that. I was hurt and I wanted to hurt back. I don't blame you for feeling bitter—I'd feel the same in your place. But I'll make it up to you somehow, I swear I will! Just give me the chance.'

Some new expression came suddenly into his eyes. He put up his hands and drew her between his knees, finding her mouth in a kiss that seared. Sharon responded with everything in her, forgetting inhibition in the surge of sheer relief which swept over her. It was going to be all right, thank heaven. It was finally going to be all right!

She made no move to stop him when he pushed her wrap from her shoulders and eased down the thin straps of her nightdress, wanting his touch with every fibre. His hands were knowledgeable, exploring every curve, every line, rousing her to a need of more. When he put her roughly away from him she was bewildered at first, until she registered his expression.

'That's enough,' he said. 'This time I'm calling the cards.' He seized her wrists in a hard grip as she moved instinctively, holding her arms away from her body. 'Why so modest all of a sudden? Nudity didn't bother you a moment ago. You were prepared to go as far as I wanted, weren't you?' He shook her when she failed to reply. 'Weren't you?'

'Yes,' she said thickly. 'But only because I thought you ...' She stopped, swallowing on the hard lump in her throat.

'Because you thought you had me in the palm of your hand again,' he finished for her. 'There's no way that's going to happen—not in any sense. I wouldn't give you the satisfaction!' He dropped his eyes to the curve of her breasts, mouth curling. 'Did you really think yourself so irresistible I wouldn't be capable of turning you down? You've a lot to learn before you come anywhere near that!'

Humiliated pride brought its own defence system into play. 'So I'll learn!' she flared.

'Not while you're still married to me, you won't. You're going to play the part of my devoted wife to the hilt, and that excludes any other men.'

'You can't make me stay with you.'

His smile was humourless. 'Where would you go? You've no job, no money of your own—and you'd hate to go crawling back to your aunt. You'll stay because you've got no choice. And you'll act the way I want you to act if you want things to stay relatively pleasant between us.' He released his grip on her and got to his feet. 'You'd better get your packing done tonight. There isn't going to be a lot of time in the morning.'

Sharon pulled up the straps of her nightdress with

trembling fingers as he disappeared into the bathroom. He was right about one thing—she wouldn't be leaving him. Not until the day she could do to him what he had done to her tonight. And she would do it. Somehow or other, she would make him want her again. Then it would be his turn to suffer!

CHAPTER FIVE

LIFE on board the *Ventura* was everything one could ask: luxurious, lazy; a floating, intimate hotel where every whim could be indulged. The yacht carried a permanent crew of four—including a chef whose creations would have done credit to any top restaurant in the world—and boasted four double staterooms in addition to the sumptuous panelled saloons. There was even a sauna on one deck, capable of taking three or four people at a time if required.

From Marseille they sailed along the Côte d'Azur at a leisurely pace which took little account of time. Sharon sunbathed a lot, slowly acquiring a golden Riviera tan which both lightened and brightened her hair in contrast. She disciplined herself to respond to any conversational overtures made by Lee in the presence of the crew, but found it difficult to maintain the same equilibrium once they were alone in their cabin together, and could only be thankful that the beds once again were singles and not the doubles she had noted in two of the other staterooms.

Lee's attitude towards her was not easy to define. In company he was always pleasant, sometimes almost appearing to have forgotten what lay between them. They swam together, and he gave her her first lesson in water-skiing, fishing her out of the water when she fell with a laughing commiseration she felt must be entirely for the benefit of the man driving the tow-boat.

John Erskine was English and in his late twenties, a cheerful extrovert who could imagine no life better than the one he was leading. He had come out to the Riviera six years ago, he told Sharon on one occasion when she expressed interest, and he wouldn't go back to England on a permanent basis for a pension. The *Ventura* was the fifth privately owned yacht he had worked on, and his favourite berth so far. With only three months out of the year at anything like full working capacity, Sharon could well see why the life was so attractive to people such as John. What she found difficult to work out was the sense in owning a vessel which for a great part of the rest of the year was simply standing idle.

'It's tax-deductible,' Lee advised dryly when she put the question to him. 'The chartering fees pay the crew and running expenses. Don't concern yourself about it.'

'I wasn't concerned,' she denied. 'Just curious. It seemed such a waste.'

He shrugged. 'No reason why you shouldn't take advantage of it yourself from time to time. Plenty of other wives do.'

'Alone?'

'If you feel like it. It's more usual to form a small party.'

Her smile was wry. 'My friends don't have that sort of freedom to come and go as they like.'

'Then find some who do.' He was silent for a moment, looking towards the distant coastline. 'We're putting into

St Tropez after lunch,' he added at length. 'I've radioed ahead and invited some people aboard for dinner. You don't have to concern yourself over the meal. Jean-Pierre decides the menu when we're entertaining. Just be ready to welcome them aboard at seven-thirty.'

'How many?' asked Sharon, trying to sound as casual as he did about it.

'Four. Two couples.'

'Married?'

'One pair is. Simone and Alain live together at present. They neither of them believe in permanent relationships.'

'Oh?' It was all she could think of to say. Lee gave her a mocking glance.

'You probably won't care for Simone. She's too much woman to be popular with her own sex.'

Sharon could imagine the type: poised, assured, sexually aware—all the things she herself was not. If her marriage to Lee had been normal—if she could have stood at his side secure in his love—then nothing else would have been important. But now? She didn't feel capable of playing the part that would be expected of her—not with any conviction. They would look at her, these people, and wonder what on earth Lee had seen in her.

St Tropez was different from what Sharon had anticipated, but still picturesque. The yacht harbour was packed with craft of all sizes and shapes, and they only just managed to secure a berth. The quayside held the most diverse motley of people Sharon had so far ever seen in one place at one time, from the well dressed to the frankly tatty. Bare breasts, she was glad to note, were not the order of the day down here.

Lee announced he was going ashore as soon as they berthed. Someone he had to see, was all the explanation proffered.

'Why don't you do the same?' he suggested to Sharon. 'Buy a new dress for tonight—have your hair done, if you feel like it. You have enough traveller's cheques?'

'I have all of them,' she said, and paused, before adding levelly, 'Are you afraid I'll let you down?'

'If you want to take it that way, you're at liberty.' He sounded impatient. 'It was just a suggestion. Most women enjoy that kind of thing, but you please yourself.'

Taking a look at herself in a mirror after he had gone, she had to acknowledge that her hair certainly could do with some professional attention. She had shampooed it that morning after a swim, but the ends needed trimming and shaping again. Finding anybody to do it at such short notice would probably prove difficult, but she could certainly try. Reluctant as she was to spend Lee's money, it was his friends she had to try to impress. Perhaps a complete change of hairstyle might help to boost her self-confidence.

There was no shortage of beauty salons in the crowded commercial quarter, all of them imposing enough from the outside to be distinctly off-putting. Sharon chose one with a name which sounded vaguely comforting, and forced herself to go inside, approaching the curved desk across one end of the luxuriously decorated reception area with a diffidence somewhat eased by the friendly smile of the blonde receptionist.

Her request in halting French for an immediate appointment was met with regret. Perhaps tomorrow might be possible, but this afternoon there was no one free to see her. Sharon thanked the girl, and came out into the hot sunshine again feeling she was probably fighting a losing battle. No salon of any repute at all was going to be able to fit her in just like that; it could even be against their policy.

She was pleasantly surprised therefore to be advised

at the next place she tried that she could take a cancellation if she cared to wait a few moments. She spent them flicking through glossy magazines in the waiting area with steadily mounting doubt in her mind. Should she really take the risk of trying to change her image a little, or should she play safe and settle for a neatening up of a style to which she was at least accustomed? The decision still wasn't made when she was called through to the private cubicle where 'André' awaited her.

Watching the man's face in the mirror as he lifted her hair in his fingers to look at it, she felt almost like apologising for daring to come in at all. The hair was, she gathered from what she could understand of his French, in a deplorable condition brought about by a lack of protection from the sun and sea. It was going to take every ounce of his skill to restore the natural oils, to say nothing of the reshaping of a style which, to judge from his expression, had been inexpertly cut in the first place.

It was then that Sharon took the plunge and asked for a complete restyle, eliciting the first gleam of real interest when she added that she would leave the choice entirely to him.

'I want to look different,' she said as he turned her head thoughtfully this way and that to gain various views of her features. And then, because she so badly needed the boost even the memory supplied, 'Someone told me not so long ago that I had good bone structure.'

True, agreed André with flattering directness, and set to work.

Gazing at herself two hours later, Sharon scarcely knew how to react. The girl looking back at her bore so little resemblance to her former self it was like seeing a stranger. After washing her hair, André had not allowed her to face the mirror again while he shaped the new style. It had taken a long time, and she had been aware of a totally new lightness in the feel of her head when he had finally allowed her to be put under the dryer, but nothing had prepared her for the shock of realisation. Not one hair had been left longer than a couple of inches, the whole thickness cunningly cut to follow the shape of her head like a close-fitting cap with slightly ragged edges. Even the colour was different, the streaks bleached by the sun blended in a glossy dapple of light and shade.

Beneath it her face seemed to have acquired new contours. The cheekbones looked higher and more prominent, the space between her eyes wider and her eyes themselves far more emphasised than they had surely ever been before.

'*Superbe!*' pronounced André in total satisfaction. '*Ma creation!*'

Which was all very well, Sharon reflected wryly, but she was the one who had to live with it. What Lee's reaction would be she hesitated to think. Yet did his opinion really matter? It was her hair to do as she liked with. And she did like it—well, perhaps like wasn't quite the word. It made her feel noticeable.

The receptionist's gasp of admiration could have been assumed, she supposed, but if so it was exceedingly well done. The size of the bill brought a gasp to her own lips, quickly stifled. On impulse, and because the other looked approachable, she asked if there was somewhere close by where she could find an outfit to suit the new style, receiving a gleam of instant understanding along with the directions.

'Julien' was a boutique just a couple of blocks away, its two front windows floored in glass tiles and displaying just the one superb garment in each. There was no price ticket attached to the black silk pyjama suit draped with such careful casualness across the scrolled, velvet-cushioned chair, and it certainly was not the kind of place where one went in just to ask how much. Sharon took her courage in both hands to open the door, determined to have enough left to say no should the cost prove even more than she anticipated.

It did, of course. In a place like St Tropez that was almost inevitable, she supposed. What she had not bargained for was the overwhelming desire to possess which swept over her the moment she saw herself in the suit. For once she had to believe the assistant's assurance that the garment was 'made for Madame!' A few hours ago it wouldn't have been, but with her hair shorn the way it was the effect was devastating. She even appeared to have gained a couple of inches in height, her body slender yet suddenly shapelier too, breasts thrusting provocatively against the thin silk top.

The dress she had worn into town had little now to recommend it; the pair of ultra-fine cotton-cord jeans in cream teamed with an amber-coloured sleeveless sweater did far more for her. The total cost gave her another shock, but she reassured herself with the thought that the wife of a man like Lee Brent would be expected to wear expensive clothes. Lee himself could hardly complain when the whole effort was really for his benefit.

Liar, she thought wryly at that point. She was being carried away by the new image, that was all. It had to stop right here, regardless of anything else. She was Lee's wife in name only.

With her dress and the new suit tucked away in a smart black bag labelled 'Julien' in gold lettering across the front, she made her way outside again, pausing to get her bearings. The traffic was heavy at this hour, driven in typical French style on throttle and brake, with the furious blare of a horn rending the air every few minutes.

A low slung red sports model swung suddenly out of the stream heading south to draw to a halt at the curb-side a few yards down from where Sharon was standing, the young man in it swivelling in his seat to gesticulate wildly to her. A moment later he was out of the car and at her side, good-looking face lit by what she could only describe as a wondrous enthusiasm.

'I can't believe it!' he exclaimed. 'It's like having a mental image come to life!' He switched suddenly to French, seeing her look of bewilderment. *'Pardon, mademoiselle. Je vous ...'*

'I'm English,' she said. 'And I've no idea what you're on about.'

'Your face, that hair—it's perfect!' He seized her chin in his hand to turn her profile on, nodding satisfaction. 'You're the Lucci girl all right!'

They were attracting curious stares by now. Sharon jerked her head free of his light grasp and took a wary step backwards away from him. 'My name isn't Lucci.'

'I know, but it could be synonymous with it.' He paused, shaking his head and laughing. 'Sorry, I got a bit carried away. I'm Dominic Foster.' Reddish brown eye-brows lifted a little at her blank expression. 'I take photographs,' he tagged on kindly. 'I thought you might have heard of me.'

'I have—of course I have!' She was suddenly breath-less, mind racing. 'I'm sorry, it just didn't register straight away.'

'My fault, pouncing on you like that. You were so exactly what I'd been looking for, I could hardly believe my luck when I saw you standing here on the roadside.' He glanced around them and made a swift decision. 'We can't talk here. There's a café just round the corner, we'll go there.'

Sharon found herself in the red car and moving off

before she had time to think about it. Not that she could
have brought herself to refuse even if she had thought
about it; she was far too intrigued for that. She stole a
glance at the rakish profile, fitting the face to what she
knew of him. Dominic Foster, one of Europe's leading
fashion photographers; married at twenty-five, divorced
at twenty-six, and that only a few months ago. A genius
with a camera, he had been called: a man capable of
turning a simple portrait into a work of art. And he had
called her perfect. But for what?

There was a parking space vacant close by the pavement café to which he took her. He left the car slewed at
an angle because it was too long to go in straight, and
found an empty table, signalling a waiter across as they
sat down.

Sharon ordered coffee to his Pernod, looking at him
expectantly as the waiter departed. 'Who, or what, is the
Lucci girl?' she asked.

He smiled. 'She's going to be a household name within
six months from now—the face to launch a whole new
range of cosmetics. She has to be different—a new look,
someone to catch the eye from a billboard or the pages
of a magazine. I nearly crashed into the car in front of
me a few minutes ago, because the driver was looking at
you instead of where he should be. That's how I saw
you myself, so I'm grateful to him.' His eyes were moving over her as he spoke, assessing detail with a professional calculation. 'I'd have sworn you were French,
though. The hair, the way you wear your clothes—sheer
chic!'

It was on the tip of her tongue to tell him she had only
just acquired that particular image, but something
stopped her. Elation was swelling like a bubble inside
her. To have any man say the things he had just said
would be flattering, but Dominic Foster was not just any

man. He actually wanted to use her face for this campaign he was talking about. It was too fantastic to take in properly.

'I've another month before I start the Lucci job,' he was saying now. 'Where will you be then? Incidentally, I don't even know your name yet?'

'Sharon,' she supplied. 'Sharon ...' she came down to earth again with a jolt as reality caught up with her, the elation vanishing ... 'Brent,' she finished on a flat note. 'I'm sorry, Mr Foster, but my husband would never agree to my taking part in anything like this.'

'You're married?' The speculation deepened. 'I'd have said ...' He broke off, smiling and lifting his shoulders. 'Surely the ultimate decision is yours? Husbands might advise, but in this day and age they can hardly command. You'd like to do it—I could see that in your eyes when I was telling you about it. Very beautiful eyes, even without the emphasis Lucci will give them.' He paused, watching her. 'Okay, let me come and talk to your husband. He's here in St Tropez with you?'

'Yes, but I don't think ...'

'Where are you staying?'

'We're down at the dock—I mean the boat is.' She gathered herself together, shaking her head regretfully. 'It wouldn't be any use.'

'It has to be. I'm not giving up so easily now I've found you. I'll take you back to the boat now and we can put it to him together.'

'No, please—not now.' Imagining Lee's reaction to the double shock gave her a sudden hysterical desire to laugh. 'He won't be there. He's seeing someone on business. And tonight we're expecting visitors.'

'Tonight's out anyway,' he said. 'I have to be in Cannes. What's your next port of call?'

'I'm not sure.'

There was a light of battle in his dark brown eyes. 'All right then, when are you due back in England?'

'About two weeks from now.'

'Then give me your address and phone number and I'll contact you there.'

'If you don't find someone else suitable in the meantime.' There was an unconscious wistfulness in her voice.

'I shan't do that.' He was smiling, but his tone held a meaningful note. 'I want you, Sharon Brent—and what I want I usually get. Now, that address.'

She gave it to him after a brief mental battle, more than half convinced that this would be the last she would hear of the whole affair. But nothing could rob her of this part of it. The glow lay over her like a warm mantle.

Looking up from the notebook where he was jotting down the details, Dominic gave a soft exclamation. 'God, if I could just catch the expression you had then for a moment!' He gazed at her with narrow-eyed concentration and came to a sudden decision. 'We've about an hour before the light goes. I'd like to get some shots of you.'

'Here?' she asked, startled.

'No, not here. We'll have to find somewhere.' He took it for granted she was going to agree, rising to his feet and flinging some notes down on the table. 'Come on!'

Once more Sharon found herself seated in the red car and being whirled through the streets, too caught up in the sheer thrill of what was happening to her to be aware of the passing scene.

Dominic finally found what he was looking for in the shape of a tiny square out towards the rear of the town. There was a stone fountain in the centre, the water falling from the lip of an urn into a walled pool. Not ideal, Dominic said, positioning her so that her head was silhouetted against the curtain of water behind her, but they were running out of light.

Sharon tried to relax tense muscles as he stalked around her viewing different angles, but felt her whole face go stiff the moment he was ready to start using the Pentax. Quite casually he began talking to her: simple inconsequential questions like did she like theatre; what did she think of French cooking as opposed to English; had she noted the way that piece of stone close by her left hand was shaped. Gradually she forgot the clicking camera and responded only to his voice—almost hypnotic in quality.

'You're a natural,' he said when he eventually called a finish to the session. He sounded excited; enthused with a new resolve. 'If these print half as good as they looked!'

Watching him repack his camera case, Sharon realised for the first time how swiftly the daylight was fading, the sunlight turning that shade of soft gold which heralded its closeness to the horizon, the shadows deep across the paving stones of the little square. They had been here a long time—too long.

'I must get back,' she said, gathering herself together. 'I'm going to be late.'

'I'll drive you back,' he said, and laughed. 'Once I find out where we are, that is. I kind of lost track of direction.'

It was gone seven when they did make the harbour. Dominic looked impressed when he saw the size of the craft berthed there.

'Which is yours?' he wanted to know.

Sharon waved a vague hand. 'Just along there.' She began to get out of the car, pausing when he reached out a hand to lightly clasp her wrist. In the gathering dusk his expression was hard to read.

'*Au revoir*, Lucci girl,' he said softly, and brought the hand he held up to his lips. 'I'll be seeing you.'

John Erskine was leaning on the rail close by the head of the gangway connecting the *Ventura* to the wharf. He straightened when Sharon began the short climb, recognition only dawning as she came level with him. Sharon had to smile at the astonishment clearly written in his eyes as he moved swiftly forward.

'Mrs Brent! I didn't realise it was you. I mean ... well, you look different!'

'I know.' The laughter bubbled from her, born of some inner emotion she could not have explained quite lucidly. 'The new me! Do you like it?'

He laughed back, catching her mood, eyes taking on a definite glint of admiration. 'You can bet! Does Mr Brent know?'

Nothing could deflate her at that moment. She shook her head. 'No, it's a surprise. Where is he?'

'In the saloon, I think.' A look of faint discomfiture came over his features. 'He said to let him know the minute you arrived.'

Sharon made a quick decision. 'You let him know,' she said. 'Tell him I've gone straight down to change.'

She reached their cabin by the forward companion-way, avoiding the saloon. Soft electric light revealed a starry-eyed face which looked back from the dressing mirror with new-found confidence. She felt ready for anything—even anticipatory. Nothing Lee could say or do was going to put her down tonight.

The black pyjama suit looked just as good here in the cabin as it had in the shop. Sharon got out the heavy gold link chain which Lee had given her for a wedding present—closing her mind against the intruding memories—and laid it ready on the dressing fitment, then took clean underwear through with her to the bathroom, closing and locking the door behind her through sheer force of habit.

It wasn't until she turned the shower off some minutes later that she heard the knocking on the door. Lee sounded angry.

'Sharon, it's almost seven-thirty! What the devil are you playing at?'

'I'm getting ready,' she called back, astonishingly unmoved. 'To meet your friends. You want me to make a good impression, don't you?'

'I want you to be there when they arrive,' he clipped.

'I will be.' She had no intention, but there was nothing to be gained by telling him that. She would make her entrance when they were all together, and let him cope with her altered appearance the best way he could. If it occurred to her to wonder if that decision smacked of a certain lack of courage to face him alone first, she kept the thought to the back of her mind.

She made certain he had left before emerging, this time turning the key in the outer door in case he came back before she was ready. It was difficult to keep a steady hand as she made up her face, especially when it came to applying mascara. Thank goodness her lashes and brows were dark enough not to need very much of it. There was nothing to do to her hair apart from running her hand over it. There wasn't enough of it left to get out of place.

Despite the assurance she had felt in the shop, she held her breath as she turned back to the mirror after putting on the black suit, dreading to find she had made some terrible mistake. It came out again on a sigh of relief when she saw the same slenderly curved shape standing there, tall and elegant in the beautifully cut trousers and deep slashed top. There was a special feel about silk next to the skin: a sensual feel.

Music drifted down from the afterdeck as she came out into the alleyway running between the staterooms. She hesitated, not quite certain whether to try the saloon first, just in case. The hearty male laugh rising over the music decided her. It wasn't Lee for certain, which meant the guests—or at least some of them—had already arrived. The time was now.

From this deck a companionway led directly up to the covered after-section, emerging between two padded banquettes. The group of people seated over towards the rear of the area behind the low, glass-topped tables failed to notice her until she was almost halfway across to them, and then conversation died abruptly.

Sharon avoided looking directly at Lee, although she was supremely conscious of his sudden move to stand up. 'I'm so sorry,' she said smilingly to the other four. 'I misjudged the time.'

Both the other men were now on their feet, the taller of the two wearing an unconcealed appreciation in his glance.

'You are worth the waiting,' he said.

Whatever his thoughts, Lee's expression was superbly controlled as he performed introductions. Simone Duval was tall and dark and self-possessed; striking rather than beautiful. She wore a simple dark blue tunic slit to the knee at both sides, her one touch of brighter colour in the unusual enamelled brooch pinned, not at the throat as most would have worn it, but on her sleeve just below the shoulder. Her greeting was lacking a little in warmth, her smile a trifle fixed.

'You're not as I imagined,' she added, without bothering to say what she had imagined.

Alain Renaud reminded Sharon a little of Jacques; not so much in looks, but certainly in manner. He was about Lee's age, and possibly three or four years older than Simone. The other couple were both in their thirties, and also French; Lee introduced them as Edie and Réal Marchand.

With Réal on one side of her and Alain on the other, dinner proved a very enjoyable occasion for Sharon. More reserved than Alain, Réal took pains to talk on subjects he obviously thought might be of special interest to her. He both knew and loved London as a city, and took it for granted that she would have at least as good a knowledge, having lived there. Laughing, Sharon had to admit that she had yet to see the Tower except from the outside, and that even Hampton Court remained an experience for future pleasure.

John Erskine served the meal to them, his stocky frame clad in a short white mess jacket and dark trousers. Simone spoke to him with smiling familiarity, underlining the fact that she was a fairly frequent guest aboard the *Ventura*. Sharon privately thought her attitude a little patronising, and sensed that John shared her opinion on catching his eye as he straightened from serving the Frenchwoman with asparagus.

They had coffee on deck in the balmy night air, burning aromatic fire sticks to keep away the insect life. During the ebb and flow of conversation, Sharon found herself at times deliberately seeking Lee's attention, looking for some response, some reaction. But whatever was in his mind, he was keeping it to himself, his manner as easy and relaxed as if everything between them was just as it should be.

It was Alain who started the dancing, drawing Sharon to her feet with a light remark about borrowing the bride for a few minutes.

The open space reserved for such manoeuvres was several feet away from where they were sitting. Taking her in his arms, he said softly, 'I have always thought of

Englishwomen as pretty creatures generally, but lacking in style. Now I must change my mind.'

'Not on my account,' she smiled. 'It took a Frenchman to achieve it for me.'

'You mean the hair? Yes, that would have to be a French creation. But I wasn't referring just to a hairstyle. It's a part of you, Sharon.' He made the name sound different, with the emphasis on the last syllable instead of the first. 'An attitude of mind. The way you presented yourself to us all tonight—that is what I mean by style.'

She laughed. 'Lee would call it simple unpunctuality! But then he's English, too.'

'You should have married a Frenchman,' Alain responded, laughing with her. 'He would know how to appreciate such gestures. A beautiful woman need never be punctual; the gratitude should be in that she came at all.' He paused before adding with disarming frankness, 'Did you marry for love?'

She was too taken aback to dissemble, her body stiffening suddenly in his arms. 'What kind of a question is that?'

'A very simple one, which you already answered. You don't have the look of a woman in love.'

Recovering swiftly, she said, 'Perhaps that's just my English reticence showing through. Are you in love with Simone?'

'But of course.' His brows lifted. 'Should that stop me from desiring other women at all?'

'Curb you, at least.'

'Curb me from taking, perhaps, but the wanting remains.' His voice deepened caressingly. 'I want you, *mignonne*.'

She was wrong, Sharon decided in that moment. Jacques played idly at this kind of thing; Alain meant it.

She kept the smile on her lips and her tone light. 'I think we'll sit this one out.'

He made no demur, taking her back to the group and dropping into general conversation as if nothing at all had passed between them. Sharon avoided Simone's eyes, and in doing so caught Lee's. Enigmatic as they were, she had the sudden conviction that he knew exactly what Alain had said to her out there on the floor.

She danced with Réal next, the two of them joined almost immediately by Lee with Simone. It was impossible to hear what they were saying to one another, but the two dark heads were very close, the Frenchwoman's face animated and expressive. Seeing them over Réal's shoulder, Sharon wondered if there had ever been a time when they had been even closer, before she met Alain— or perhaps even since. Alain himself seemed totally unconcerned by any such notion, applying his present attentions to Edie, who had declined to move on to the floor.

Réal spoke English with more precision but less ease than both Alain and Simone. It made him sound a little stilted now as he said: 'We were delighted to hear that Lee had found the incentive to take a wife at last. You were, as he would say himself, worth waiting for.'

'Well, thank you.' Sharon was touched by the man's obvious sincerity, yet was also conscious of feeling a fraud in the circumstances. She wondered fleetingly if Réal would have thought the original model worth waiting for. Certainly she had never received the same amount of attention—except perhaps from Jacques. The memory of Dominic Foster's professional admiration was something to be hugged to herself in moments of self-doubt from now on—a bolster against the world. Even if she never saw him again that could never be taken away from her. But she hoped she would see him again. Regardless of what trouble it caused, she wanted desperately to be the Lucci girl. More desperately than she had ever wanted anything.

'How long have you known Lee?' she asked.

'Many years. We were business acquaintances first through our respective fathers, and then we became friends too. Edie is very fond of your husband.'

'And Simone?' Sharon met his eyes blandly, having already registered a reaction through the hand at her back. 'Is she in business too?'

'Not in the same line.' Réal looked as if he weren't quite sure whether the questions were innocent or not. 'She owns a string of boutiques named Julien.'

'Good heavens, I got this from there!'

'It looks expensive enough.' His eyes twinkled. 'Edie buys there only rarely, I am glad to say.' He moved her suddenly across the floor closer to the other couple, breaking in on the conversation in progress. 'You have a client in Sharon, Simone. I'm surprised you don't recognise your own trademark.'

The dark eyes met Sharon's briefly, the smile on her lips not touching them. 'As a matter of fact, I did,' she said. 'One remembers certain items because they are extra special. You have very good taste.'

'Very costly ones too.' Lee's tone was light. 'Your prices were always exorbitant, Simone.'

'For true quality one must be prepared to pay through the nose,' came the unperturbed retort. 'Would you begrudge your wife so little?'

Sharon's laugh sounded forced to her own ears. 'He begrudges me nothing, do you, Lee?'

His glance went over her as she stood within the circle of Réal's arms, his smile taking on a new slant. 'Who could?'

In the small silence, Réal released his hold on Sharon

and held out a hand to Simone instead. 'I think we will allow the bride and groom to finish the dance together. After all, this is their honeymoon. Who are we to keep them apart!'

Whatever the other woman's thoughts on the subject, there was little she could do but put on a good face and go along with the suggestion, leaving Sharon to move reluctantly into Lee's arms.

'Not so tense,' he said softly, drawing her close to put his face against her hair. 'We don't want to disappoint the audience, do we? We're newly married and madly in love. Can't you act that part?'

Despite herself, she was stirred by his closeness, by the feel of the lean hard body moving against hers. Recklessness swept over her, sliding her arms up over his shoulders until she could feel the strong beat of his heart pulsing right through her.

'Is this better?' she murmured.

'Infinitely.' There was a note in his voice which made her quiver deep down in the pit of her stomach and sent a tingling sensation the length of her limbs. 'You're wearing very little under this.'

'It isn't meant to have a lot worn under it.' She was making every effort to stay in command of her own senses. 'Are you going to comment on my new hairstyle, or didn't you notice?'

'It would have been very difficult not to notice. That was the intention, wasn't it?' He didn't wait for an answer. 'It appears to have altered you in more ways than one.'

'For better or for worse?'

'It depends on the point of view. Whatever girlishness was left in you before, it's gone now.'

She stiffened a little. 'You mean I look obvious?'

'I mean you look ... aware. Alain noted it too. He

wouldn't have paid the same attention to the girl who went to town this afternoon.' He paused then, tone altering a little. 'It's more than just the hair and the outfit. Something else happened to you this afternoon.'

'That's right.' She gave him a veiled glance, not yet ready to reveal the true source of her inner glow. 'I spent a lot of money—your money. It's a mixture of guilt and complacency, I suppose.'

He laughed dryly. 'I can believe the last better than the first. But don't get too complacent, I'm not that easily led.'

Sharon moved away from him as far as his arms would allow her. She said low-toned, 'If you were right about my motives I'd have hardly been concerned by what Lora said.'

'Your pride was stung, that was all. You'd liked the idea of having me in love with you even if you didn't return the feeling.'

'That isn't true! I was hurt because I loved you.'

'Stop deluding yourself. If you'd loved me, you'd have given me at least a chance to explain.' He shook his head, eyes coolly mocking. 'Your trouble was you didn't have the courage of your convictions. If you'd forced yourself over the actual physical reluctance to sleep with a man you didn't have any feeling for, you'd have found you could enjoy it regardless and I might never have known the difference. The point now is I do know, so you're not going to change anything by getting into bed with me. Just so long as that's clear.'

Her voice felt tight in her throat. 'I've no intention of getting into bed with you!'

'We'll see.' Lee brought her back against him again, holding her in a way which made it impossible to resist without making it obvious to everyone else. 'I've an urge to find out just how far the reluctance goes.'

It was well past midnight before anyone made a move to go. Simone took leave of Lee with a regret not in the least tempered by the presence of others.

'It's been a good evening,' she said. 'Almost like old times. Shall you be calling in again on your way back to Marseille.'

'Perhaps,' he said. 'It depends on how much time we have in hand. Next time we come we could make up a party and spend a few days in Monte Carlo.'

'Pity you're still on your honeymoon,' remarked Alain lightly, 'or we'd have taken you up on that offer right now.' His smile was for Sharon, slow and meaningful. 'I'll look forward to that next time.'

Sharon avoided Lee's eyes when they were finally alone again, and turned away.

'I'm going to bed,' she announced shortly.

'I know.' His tone was level. 'I'm coming with you.'

She looked at him then, registering the mocking gleam with a jerk of her heart. 'No, you're not!'

'We'll discuss it below,' he said as John came out to clear away the glasses on the afterdeck. 'Voices carry too far at night.'

That was true enough. Standing there, she could hear people talking on the next boat quite clearly. Further down the line, music was playing, the sound of laughter floating over the top. In port the only real privacy was below.

She went ahead of Lee, nerving herself for the moments ahead. He hadn't been joking earlier and he wasn't joking now, but she was damned if she was going to go along with him. Yet she couldn't deny the part of her that wanted him either. That was something else she was going to have to fight.

He shut the door quietly behind him when they reached

the cabin, not bothering to try and hide the click of the lock as he turned the key.

'Just so you don't get any ideas about leaving,' he said. He stayed where he was for a moment, studying her, mouth tilting a little. 'Whoever devised that style for you certainly knew what he was about. Very few could get away with it. I shouldn't have thought you could, until I saw it with my own eyes.'

'It wasn't done for your sake,' she came back. 'It was for my own.'

'Whatever the reason, it had the same effect. I wasn't the only one who felt the adrenalin start rising when you came out on deck tonight. You knocked Alain for six.'

'That was only physical.'

'I know it was only physical. Just as what happened between us when we were dancing was only physical.' He paused, tone softening. 'Just as this now is purely physical.'

She watched him move away from the door, taking off his dinner jacket as he did so to toss it over a chair. His tie followed.

'I am *not* going to sleep with you, Lee,' she said desperately, and saw his smile come again.

'Not for some time, I agree.' He stopped unbuttoning his shirt and came over to her, taking her by the arms to draw her to him. 'There's a small matter of a lost wedding night to take care of first.'

Her resistance didn't last long—he gave it no opportunity. Helplessly she found herself kissing him back, her body surrendering itself into his hands with neither will nor desire to deny him.

He undressed her without undue haste, a flame springing in his eyes when he looked at her.

'Beautiful all over,' he murmured. 'Long-limbed and

lovely! Don't shrink away from me. I want to look at you—drink you in.'

'Lee,' her voice was a whisper, 'please . . .'

He laughed softly and brought her back hard against him, fingers running the length of her spine. 'All right, so you undress me.'

'I . . . can't.'

She could because he made her, guiding her hands until the last garment was gone while between times kissing her neck, her throat, the lobes of her ears, running the tip of his tongue inside the latter until her whole body felt on fire. Only then did he lift her up and take her to the bed, laying her on the cover and coming down beside her.

'Stop trembling,' he said into her hair. 'I'm not going to hurt you. I won't do anything before you're completely ready for it. Just relax and let me rouse you. You're half-way there already.'

'Tell me you love me,' she pleaded. 'Even if it isn't true, just say it.'

'No.' He hadn't raised his voice, but there was an inflexible note to it. 'And don't try saying it to me either, because I don't want to hear it. You're here like this with me because you want what I want, and for no other reason.' His tone roughened along with his hands as she tried to push him away. 'It's too late to start changing your mind now. I'm not letting you go. It's your choice, Sharon—either you enjoy it or you suffer it. Personally, I'd as soon you enjoyed it.'

In spite of herself, she could feel the glow rising in her again under his touch. She wanted to hate him, but she couldn't summon the strength. She doubted if it would have made any difference anyway.

Emotion gave way to sensation, ripple after ripple of it

running like quicksilver through her veins. She felt the beat of his heart against her breast as his weight came over her, and knew a momentary resistance swiftly dispelled by the warmth of his mouth on hers again.

She kissed him back hungrily, all restraint gone from her now. Agony seized her and as swiftly released her, leaving her free to soar into a mindless world of pleasure.

Lee was back in his own bed when Sharon awoke early next morning. She lay there in the soft light looking across at him, remembering the night with a confusion of feeling inside her. He had made love to her again before finally sleeping, because the first time, he had said, was never the best for a woman. He was right about that, she thought now, body stirring restlessly. It had been wonderful—an experience beyond anything she had ever anticipated. If it had really been their wedding night, with all its attendant emotions, she would have been the happiest, most contented person in the world right now.

As if sensing her eyes on him, he opened his own, coming awake all of a piece with none of the momentary blankness common in many. There was knowledge in the glance he sent winging over her; a visual growth of desire.

'He said softly, 'Come over here.'

She rolled on to her back away from him, fighting the misery which swept her. 'That's all you want me for, isn't it?'

'It's all we have,' he said on a harder note. 'So let's make the most of it. Pay your dues and you can spend as much as you like.'

'Even at Julien's?'

'That might be difficult. We're leaving St Tropez today.'

'Poor Simone.' Her voice sounded cracked. 'I won't say

she doesn't know what she's missing, because I'm quite sure she does. Was she satisfactory in bed too?'

'Very,' His tone was dry. 'And satisfactory isn't quite the term I'd apply to you—not yet. As I said the other night, there's a lot you have to learn.'

'Which you also said you'd no intention of teaching me.'

'That was then, this is now. Moods change.' He threw back the covers in a decisive gesture. 'So I'll come to you.'

There was less gentleness in him than there had been the night before, but he could still make her respond. Afterwards, lying in his arms with his weight still pinning her, she said thickly, 'You're a bastard, Lee,' and heard his short laugh.

'If I am you made me one. Anyway, consider the bright side. You could have hated everything I've done to you.'

'That could still happen.'

'Then that will be your bad luck.' His breath was warm against her cheek, his lips just brushing the skin. 'I've enjoyed having you, darling, and I'm going to go on enjoying you. It's a small enough exchange for what you'll be getting.'

'I don't want anything,' she denied on a note of desperation. 'Lee, I really don't . . .'

'Don't start that line again; it won't work. You acquired a new look and you're going to need to dress to it. You recognised that much yourself when you bought that black pyjama suit.' He pushed himself upright and reached for the silk dressing gown draped across the arm of a nearby chair. 'I think a lot of people are going to be in for a shock when we get back home. I took away a sweet young innocent and brought back a siren.' His smile held irony. 'I wonder which my father is going to prefer?'

CHAPTER SIX

THEY had been at White Ladies two days before Richard Brent came out to the house. He found Sharon in the music room tinkering idly with the piano keys, the afternoon sunlight bright on her hair. His reaction was so comically taken aback she had to laugh.

'Did you think you'd come to the wrong house?' she asked, moving to greet him. 'It's my French look!'

'It's more than a look,' he said, studying her with an odd expression. 'It's a whole new person. Did Lee suggest the change?'

'No, it was my own idea.' She quirked an eyebrow. 'Don't you like it?'

'I'm not sure,' he admitted cautiously. 'I liked the other Sharon. I'll have to get to know this one all over again.'

'You never really knew me before,' she said on a light note. 'There wasn't time. Let me get you a drink—or would you rather have tea?'

'I'll settle for the tea, considering the time.'

'It should be here in a few minutes. I assume Mrs Reynolds knows you're here?'

'Yes, I saw her in the hallway.' He smiled, taking a seat. 'I got the distinct impression I should have rung the doorbell and waited, rather than just walking in. Suppose she's quite right too—after all, I'm not the master of the house any more. How do you get along with her?'

116

'We're coming to terms.' She added with emphasis, 'And you walk in any time you want to. It's still your house really.'

'No, it isn't. It's yours and Lee's, all clear and legal.' He paused expectantly. 'Isn't he here at all?'

'He went to see someone.'

'Who?'

'I'm not sure.' She heard the tinkle of teacups out in the hall with relief. 'Business, I gathered.'

'On a Sunday afternoon?' Richard shook his head. 'I'll have to have words with that son of mine. You'll be on your own enough without leaving you at the week-ends too.'

'He shouldn't be long,' Sharon said hurriedly. 'Anyway, you'll stay on to dinner, won't you?'

'Can't be done, I'm afraid, much as I'd love to. Lorna is staying at Copperlea with Lora and Jason and I'm invited there. My daughter doesn't despair of getting us both to reconcile our differences some day. Far too late, of course, but like Lee she has this managing streak.'

She smiled. 'And Father won't be managed.'

'Only if it's the way he wants to go.' He got to his feet as the door opened, moving quickly to take the tray from the housekeeper's hands. 'Let me relieve you of that. Thank you, Mrs Reynolds. Now you can go and put your feet up.'

Sharon was laughing when he came back with the tray, having firmly closed the door again. 'I wish I could handle her like that. I'm still not sure which one of us is really mistress of the house!'

'You are, my dear, make no mistake about it. If you're having trouble with the woman, get rid of her, and find someone else to run the place.'

'Oh, I wouldn't bother doing that. I could do the job myself.'

'Too tying. You can think about domesticity when you start a family.' He took the filled cup from her, eyes on her face. 'You are planning on having children, aren't you?'

'Eventually.' Her face felt stiff. 'Do you have a yen to be a grandfather?'

'It might be rather nice—all the fun with none of the responsibilities. Bringing up children is no picnic. They don't always turn out the way one plans.'

'Didn't Lee?' Sharon asked lightly, and her father-in-law laughed and shook his head.

'Some ways, yes. Others ... well, you're his wife. I probably don't have to tell you how completely immovable he can be at times. He didn't get that from me. I believe in keeping an open mind.' He studied her averted face, tone altering. 'I hope he's making you happy.'

'Of course.' She met his eyes and gave a small wry shrug, knowing him not wholly deceived. 'We have our differences, like everyone does, but we're learning to adjust.'

'Both, or just you?' he demanded bluntly. 'No, don't bother answering that. The way you handle him is your own concern.'

Sharon hadn't meant to say it, but somehow it was dragged from her. 'Why did he have to be married before you'd hand over control of the Company?'

It was a moment before he answered, his expression taking on a certain enlightenment.

'He needed an anchor,' he said at length. 'Some personal responsibility. He has a brilliant mind for business, and he's more than capable of taking over control, but he allowed himself too many ... distractions.'

'Especially of the female variety.' She smiled at the fleeting look in his eyes. 'It's all right, I'm quite well aware of it. I may have seemed pretty ingenuous when you first met me, but I wasn't blind enough to imagine I was the first girl in his life.'

'You were the first one he ever felt deeply about,' came the gruff retort. 'I suspected it when he phoned to tell me about you, and I was sure of it when I saw you. You were so different from anyone I'd seen him with before, Sharon. Young and unsophisticated, so terribly unsure of yourself—though not lacking in backbone either.'

'Not the type to inspire lust, so it had to be love.'

'Not the type to come out with a remark like that for certain.' He was looking at her with narrowed regard. 'Cynicism usually takes more than a few weeks to develop.'

Her face flushed a little. 'I'm sorry—I was trying to be clever. I know what you mean.'

'So I can take it you still love him?'

'Yes.' There was little else she could say. With Lee she had run a whole gamut of emotions. If put together they constituted a whole, then yes, she loved him.

'Good.' There was a familiar glint of steel in the grey eyes. 'I'd hate to think I was wrong about that stabilising influence.'

He changed the subject after that, asking her how she had enjoyed the Riviera resorts; what they had done there, whom she had met. At one point Sharon was tempted to tell him about Dominic Foster, but two things held her back. First, he might mention the matter to Lee at some time and wonder why she hadn't told him herself, and second, Dominic had yet to contact her. What she was going to do if and when he did so remained open to doubt. There was little point in meeting that particular problem before it arose.

They were still sitting there chatting when Lee returned just before six. He greeted his father easily, bending over the back of Sharon's chair to drop a light kiss on the top of her head.

'What do you think of the new model?' he asked.

'I'm still trying to decide,' the other said on a somewhat ambiguous note. 'Obviously you approve.'

'One grows accustomed to anything in time.' He moved across to the drinks tray. 'I have to admit, it took some mental adjustment. Who's going to join me?'

Sharon followed Richard's lead, unwilling to be the odd man out. Meeting Lee's gaze as he put the sherry glass in her hand, she said quickly, 'I asked your father to stay for dinner, but he isn't able.'

'One of Lora's family "at homes",' Richard explained. 'Jason's parents and her own. You realise you'll not be let off the hook for long, of course?'

'That's all right. We'll take the initiative out of her hands and invite them over here first.' Lee had perched himself on the arm of Sharon's chair, supporting himself with one arm across the back behind her head. 'What do you say, darling? Next week?'

'Weekend,' Richard corrected. 'You're in Copenhagen on Tuesday, remember. Doubt if you'll get through much before Thursday evening.' He caught Sharon's change of expression and added, 'Didn't he tell you?'

She shook her head, feeling the nape of her neck brush against his jacket sleeve. 'Not yet.'

'I was waiting for the right moment,' Lee said imperturbably. 'Tell Lora Saturday, then. Mother too, if she feels in the mood. Did you say she was staying with Lora and Jason?'

'I didn't, but she is. For how long I've no idea.' Richard looked at Sharon and smiled. 'I shan't tell any of them about the new look. I'll enjoy seeing their expressions when you spring it on them!'

He left around seven. Turning back from the main

door after seeing him off down the drive, Sharon moved abruptly from under the weight of Lee's arm about her shoulders.

'There's no more need for that sort of thing,' she said. 'He's gone. You can be yourself again.'

'I am being myself,' he returned on an amicable note which drew her eyes to his face in quick suspicion. 'I like touching you.' He tipped up her face with a finger under her chin and kissed her on the lips, smiling at her rigid lack of response. 'Don't challenge me that way or I'll cancel dinner and take you upstairs instead—that would give Mrs Reynolds food for thought!'

'Can't you think of anything else?' she demanded with sarcasm.

'When I'm with you, no, not a lot. There's something about making love to you that I never got from anyone else. Perhaps it's knowing just how much you hate what I can do to you that provides the extra thrill.' Unexpectedly he let her go. 'I can wait. How long had Father been here when I came?'

'A couple of hours.' Deprived of contact with him, irrationally she wanted it back. 'He wanted to know if you were making me happy.'

'And what did you tell him?'

'Oh, ecstatically! What else?'

Lee eyed her for a long hard moment. 'That's what I'm asking.'

The spark faded, leaving her flat. 'You don't have to worry. So far as he's concerned our marriage is following predictable lines. The first time we met he said living with a man like you could be hell. He obviously doesn't expect instant harmony.'

'Perhaps as well, considering. We'll have to work on developing some.'

'You mean a good pretence of it, don't you?'

'All right, a pretence of it.' He sounded suddenly indifferent. 'Providing it gains the same end. I'm going up to change. Could be my last relaxed evening for some time to come.'

Sharon had looked forward to a day spent on her own, but before it was halfway through she found herself restless and bored. The fine weather had given way to grey cloud and drizzle that kept her indoors. Being unable to drive was going to be a real drawback, she realised disconsolately. And learning took so long, even if an instructor was available. Certainly she had no intention of asking Lee to teach her.

By four she was beginning to anticipate his return with something less than aversion, and was hard put to it to conceal her disappointment when he rang through at six to say he was still tied up and not to wait dinner for him. She ate her own meal at a small table set in front of the sitting room fire, listening to the patter of rain against the windows and almost wishing they were back on the Côte d'Azur.

The last couple of weeks had been an experience she would not have missed despite the accompanying problems. Port Grimaud, Cannes, Antibes, Nice—they had visited them all, staying one night or sometimes two; hiring cars to drive through countryside filled with the perfume of orange and eucalyptus, lemon and laurel to the hill villages and colourful little towns; swimming from the dazzling white beaches at Cavalaire and Le Lavandou, enjoying the off-season quietness.

And then there had been Monte Carlo, two days and nights of it, dining at the Casino, watching the gamblers, the magnificently gowned and jewelled women. The dress she had worn that second and last night was hanging now in the wardrobe upstairs along with all the other garments she had acquired. It had held its own, she knew. And so had the diamond collar Lee had given her to go with it. Necessary darling, he'd said, as he fastened it about her neck.

Thinking about that moment now, Sharon recalled how superb he had looked in evening dress: the undeniable feeling of pride she had experienced when other women had looked at him. He had introduced her to several people during the course of the evening, and received many congratulations on his choice of a bride. There had been invitations too, the latter regretfully declined on the grounds that they had to get back to Marseille, but nonetheless sincere. What it all boiled down to was acceptance: she fitted in. Confidence had bloomed in her from there on in.

And she was going to need all of it, she acknowledged, to face both other female members of the Brent family at the weekend. Refusing to allow the thought to daunt her, she began considering the question of the menu. Mrs Reynolds was an excellent cook, but she wasn't in Jean-Pierre's class. Still, it should be possible to sort out something reasonably impressive without overtaxing her capabilities.

It was past nine before Lee finally put in an appearance. He looked tired, Sharon thought. He said he had eaten in town, and helped himself to a drink, tossing half of it back in one pull before sinking into a chair with his legs stretched out and a look of relief on his face.

'That's better,' he said. 'I'm down on stamina. Still, at least I'm clear for the week.'

'What time are you leaving?' Sharon asked diffidently. 'Do you have to go in to the office first?'

He shook his head without lifting it from the chair back. 'I'm on a ten o'clock flight, I'll need to leave here no later than eight. Tell Mrs Reynolds just scrambled

eggs and toast, will you, around seven-thirty. No need
for you to get up, of course. You can turn over and go
back to sleep.'

'I never can once I'm awake,' she said, and hesitated
before adding. 'Actually, I thought I'd make an effort
and go up north for a couple of days while you're away.'

He looked at her then, brows lifted. 'To see your aunt
and uncle?'

'Yes.'

'I assume you'd rather I didn't meet them. Scared I
might look down on them?'

She met his gaze steadily. 'No, I'm not scared of that.
I think you'd rather like Uncle Brian. He's one of those
very big, very quiet men who take life just as it comes.
I can never remember him losing his temper, or even getting more than mildly annoyed.'

'But your aunt is another matter. What makes you so
sure she even wants to see you again?'

'I'm not sure. But neither can I just leave it at that. I
spent sixteen years of my life with them, and can't say I
was unhappy during them. I'd like to straighten things
out if I can.'

'I'd try phoning them first to make sure you don't have
a wasted journey.'

'They're not on the phone. I contacted them through a
neighbour to tell them about the wedding plans.' She
said it without a tremor. 'I wouldn't want the whole road
to know I'm visiting.'

Lee shrugged as if tiring of the subject. 'Please yourself. I should be back on Friday morning, although I'll
probably go straight in to the office from the airport.
Don't forget about the dinner party on Saturday.'

'I haven't.' She would, Sharon reflected dryly, have
found it very difficult. 'I'll give Mrs Reynolds the menu
before I go, then she can be thinking about it. Your

family don't have any special aversions, do they?'

'Not that I can think of. Whatever you do, my mother will be sure to find something not to her taste.'

'Because I planned it?'

He didn't attempt to deny the insinuation. 'Not especially. She does it everywhere. In her view, unmitigated praise never did anything but harm in the long run. Don't let it worry you—we shan't be seeing all that much of her. She and I never were very close at the best of times.' The grin was fleeting. 'I was far too rough and boisterous a youth.' Meeting her glance, he said, 'You look sceptical.'

'I am,' she returned frankly. 'Boisterousness suggests a lack of control, and I doubt if you ever suffered from that. Cool self-assurance I could go along with.'

There was an unreadable expression in the grey eyes. 'You'd like to see me lose control.'

'It might make you a little more understanding of others.'

Lee laughed softly and put down his glass. 'It's enough that I can make you lose it. An early night might not be a bad idea considering we'll both be up and away in the morning.'

Sharon stayed where she was, refusing to let any reaction show. 'I'm not ready for bed yet.'

'Then we'll lock the door and make love right here in front of the fire,' he said. 'I need something to carry me through the next few days.'

Her heart was beating as fast as it always did at moments like this, desire and rejection warring within her. 'You don't mean you're considering staying celibate that long!'

For a moment he continued to study her, the contraction of his jawline the only outer indication of his feelings. 'Perhaps you're right,' he said at last. 'A change is as good as a rest.' He pressed himself to his feet, the movement abrupt. 'I'm going up anyway.'

Sharon bit her lip as he left the room. She had asked for it, yet now that she had it where was the satisfaction? Why couldn't she bring herself to accept the limitations of their relationship, and make the best of them? Plenty of other women would envy her what she had, and consider it more than enough. How many ever had everything?

There was a part of her now which wanted badly to get up and follow Lee upstairs, to feel those oh, so wonderfully strong and sensitive hands of his on her body, his lips on hers; to know the tumult of emotion growing inside her until it swept her up and over the crest into sheer heaven. But there was also another part which needed more than just physical love, and right now that was the stronger of the two. It wouldn't allow her to give in.

In any case, Lee would probably gain quite a lot of satisfaction from turning her down if she did go to him. The hold she had on him might be fairly strong, but it wasn't irresistible. He had just proved that.

Impasse, she conceded with a sigh. If anything at all was to be made of this marriage of theirs, she was going to have to be the one to make all the sacrifices. Always providing Lee intended it to last beyond the time when his father retired, of course. Once he had control of the Company there would be no further need for subterfuge of any kind.

He was asleep when she finally went up to their room around eleven-thirty, a rounded hump under the covers, head turned away from the door. Sharon prepared for bed in the bathroom so as not to disturb him with a light, feeling her way across to slide gently beneath her side of the sheets and ease her body into a reclining position, breath released on a small sigh when she achieved it.

Darkness lay thick and heavy about her. Normally she would have opened the curtains a little way to let in the moonlight because she couldn't bear sleeping in total darkness. Too late to think about that now. Her eyes would become accustomed to it soon enough. Sleep seemed a million miles off. She was too conscious of the man lying so close and yet so far away, still and silent. Even his breathing was scarcely audible.

The suddenness of his movement took her completely by surprise. She felt the sheet flung back, and then the hardness of his fingers fastening into the neckline of her brief cotton nightdress to rip it down to the hemline in one ruthless pull. Too stunned to make any sound of protest, she saw him looming over her, big and dark and utterly without mercy. There was no resisting his strength and purpose; all she could do was go along with it, her cry muffled by the pressure of his mouth and the driving weight of his body.

It was over quickly, and he didn't linger, rolling away from her to lie on his back with his breath coming harshly.

'That's what it could be,' he muttered. 'You'd better make up your mind which you prefer before I get back.'

Sharon was motionless, body and mind aching in unison. 'You had no right,' she got out through stiff lips. 'You don't own me, Lee!'

'No, I don't. But neither will I take rejection on the terms you dish it out under.' His voice was low and hard. 'If you want to say no, *say* it—clearly and simply. Don't try getting at me the way you did tonight.'

He said nothing more. The silence was oppressive. After a moment or two, Sharon forced her limbs into movement, getting out of the bed to go into the bathroom and bolt the door between them.

Jaw clenched, she stuffed the torn nightdress into the laundry basket and ran the shower, stepping under it without bothering about a cap, the warmth of the water her only desire. She stayed under until the trembling had stopped, but nothing could soothe away the hurt from her mind. Lee had waited for her with the one intention—a calculated assault. Nothing she had said or done could excuse that. Nothing!

A vigorous towelling almost dried her hair. The only robe in the bathroom was Lee's white one. She put it on, belting it tightly about her waist before opening the door, leaving the light on so that she could see where she was.

He was lying in what appeared to be the exact same position, face upturned to the ceiling. Sharon was halfway across the room before he spoke.

'Where are you going?'

'To find another bed,' she said without looking back.

'No, you're not.' He came up on one elbow. 'You stay right here.'

'Not with you!' The revulsion quivered in her voice. 'Not ever again with *you*!'

Lee reached her as she got the door open, kicking it closed again as he swung her up in his arms to carry her back to the bed.

'You're staying here,' he repeated, dropping her on to the pillows.

'So you can rape me again?' she shot at him, and saw a muscle jerk at the side of his mouth. 'I hope you're proud of yourself!'

'You had it coming,' he said. 'I should have taken you that way back at Lucerne when I first found out about your scheming little mind. Or are you still trying to make out that was a mistake?'

'No.' She said it between her teeth. 'I never loved you,

Lee Brent. I never could love a man like you! After tonight I don't want you near me again. Do you hear? If you so much as touch me, I'll go to your father and tell him just what kind of son he has. You can say goodbye to the presidency then—he wouldn't think you fit to take over from him!'

It was a long moment before he moved. His face had gone totally blank, his eyes cold. 'You don't need to find another bed,' he said. 'I will. I'll file for a separation order as soon as I get back. If you decide to stay north, you'll have to contact me with an address where you can be reached. Otherwise, you'd better start thinking about where you'd like to live.'

Her chest felt tight as a drum, her throat so dry she could barely get the words out 'Lee, I . . .'

'No, that's it.' His tone was final. 'I've had it. To hell with the presidency. To hell with the whole damned business!'

He was gone before she could find anything to say. There was nothing *to* say. They were finished, and she had finished them, finally and irrevocably. The knowledge lay on her like a tangible weight.

She was awake when Lee came in at seven for his things, but she feigned sleep, lying on her stomach with her face half buried in the pillow. Listening to the sounds of his movements, she wished she had the courage to face him, to ask him to forget last night and start again when he got back from Denmark. Yet even if they did start again what was the use? Lee had loved something in her that she could never recapture no matter how hard she tried. She could make him want her, but that was all— and perhaps not even that now.

It seemed an age until the door finally closed. He hadn't said a word yet she had the feeling he had known she was not asleep. She came slowly to a sitting position, hugging her knees as she tried to sort out the next move. Obviously the trip north had to be off for the present. There was little use in seeing her aunt and uncle until something definite had been arranged—which left her with three days to fill. It wasn't going to be easy.

It was a long and fraught morning, hardly helped by the continuing bad weather. Sharon was in the music room when the telephone rang a little before ten-thirty. She lifted the receiver cautiously. Lee would be in the air by now, unless there had been a delay.

The voice was male and vaguely familiar. 'Am I speaking to Sharon Brent?'

'Yes,' she admitted, and the voice took on a warmer note.

'Thought I recognised you. It's Dominic Foster here.' He waited, then added quizzically, 'Don't you remember me?'

'Yes, I remember.' For someone whose breath had been taken away, she sounded remarkably calm, Sharon reflected. 'I just didn't expect you to call, that's all.'

'Why not? I told you I'd found my Lucci girl. When it comes to work, I'm no fickle character.' He paused again, more briefly this time. 'Did you mention the job to your husband?'

Standing there, Sharon felt sudden resolve take hold of her. 'No,' she said. 'But it isn't important.'

'Oh?' There was speculation in the word. 'Then I take it you're ready to talk terms?'

'I'm ready to be the Lucci girl,' she said. 'Regardless of terms.'

'Well, you'll find them very generous anyway. This is a high-budget project. How long will it take you to get into town?'

'Today?'

'That's right. They've seen those shots I took of you

in St Tropez, now they'd like to meet the original.'

Sharon was cautious. 'So I haven't actually got the job yet.'

'All bar signing the contract. Can you make it for lunch first?'

Ridiculously she found herself nodding. 'I should think so.'

'Right, I'll meet you at one. Rules in Maiden Lane. Know it?'

'Know of it,' she said, borrowing his tone. 'I'll be there.'

Replacing the receiver, she stood for a moment to collect her thoughts, aware of a mingled sense of apprehension and excitement. This way could lie independence: freedom to take that separation Lee had spoken of under her own initiative. Why go on hoping for any improvement in their relationship? It wasn't going to improve. They might as well cut their losses now before things got any worse—if it were possible for that to happen.

Fired by a new purpose, she ordered a taxi to pick her up at eleven-thirty for the noon train, and went upstairs to find something to wear. It had to be a special outfit but not too dressy: something to impress without taking over.

She took extra care with her make-up before getting into the silky Italian knit dress and jacket which had been her final choice. The dress was pale beige with a drawstring waistline and smoothly fitting skirt, the jacket two-tone, cardigan style. With it she teamed oyster accessories. At least the rain had stopped; that might be a good omen. Regardless of what Dominic had said, it surely depended on whether or not these Lucci people liked her when they saw her in the flesh, so to speak. They had to like her. The immediate future depended upon it.

CHAPTER SEVEN

Dominic was just as she remembered him. He was talking with some other men at the bar when she entered the restaurant, but he broke off at once to come and greet her.

'You look very beautiful, and very expensive,' he said approvingly when they were seated. 'Just the ticket. Lucci products aren't going to be cheap. They're designed to appeal to the woman who believes in putting only the best on her skin, and the price has to reflect that worth.'

'Are they really any better than any other cosmetic line in that bracket?' Sharon asked, and he grinned.

'It's up to us to make people believe they are. Where Joe, or in this case Jill public loses out is in not having the kind of expert help in applying the stuff that you'll be getting. They'll want you to have the works this afternoon just to see what can be done, so I hope you're not in any hurry to get back?'

Sharon moved her head negatively. 'None at all.'

He studied her for a moment, eyes reflective. 'Husband out of town?'

'He's in Copenhagen,' she stated on a note which should have discouraged further questions, but the good-looking face opposite betrayed no sign of taking the hint.

'I've been doing some homework since we met. You married Lee Brent of Brent Incorporated less than a month ago. Which makes what you said on the phone this morning rather strange.'

'What did I say?' Sharon hedged.

'I think you remember perfectly well.' He waited, then smiled and shrugged. 'Obviously the honeymoon is over in more ways than one. Money isn't everything.'

Anger flared in her eyes. 'I didn't marry him for that reason!'

'Maybe not wholly, but I'll bet it helped blind you to certain things about him. Same way I let myself be blinded five years ago when I met Diane Hall. Luckily she was already married, so I didn't get in as deep as you did. It took me about the same time as you to discover that the pros nowhere near outweighed the cons, and another six months to make myself admit it and start making it on my own.' His grin was disarming. 'Mind you, I'd gained quite a lot materially from the relationship in the meantime—including the kind of equipment I'd never have acquired otherwise—so you could say it was all worthwhile. I gave six months of my youth in exchange for all this. Not a bad swap, I'd say.'

'You got where you are by your own talents,' Sharon protested.

'Aided and assisted by money—just as money made you the way you look today. Your wedding photograph certainly showed a different image.'

'Perhaps the photographer didn't have your eye for a good angle.'

He laughed appreciatively. 'You know, you've changed again since St Tropez. Or perhaps matured a little might be a better way of putting it. Make a success of this job and you won't have to rely on anyone for anything again. In all due modesty, the fact that I discovered you provides the "open sesame". You're starting at the top!'

'From where I can only go down,' Sharon rejoined, striving for a suitably light note. 'I'll take it a step at a time, thanks. Who exactly will be vetting me this after-noon?'

He accepted the change of direction without demur. 'There's Roger Venables, the managing director, for one, and Lucy Wells in charge of promotions for another. Others too, of course, but they're the ones you'll be deal-ing with directly. To them you're simply the canvas on which they propose presenting their wares, so don't feel insulted if they tend towards the impersonal. They're coming to the studio at three-thirty, by the way. If we get back there about three you can relax for half an hour beforehand.'

Her smile was wry. 'I shan't be able to relax, I'll be too nervous.'

'You don't have to be nervous—not of anything. Just keep telling yourself that Dominic Foster considers you one of the most photogenically perfect models he ever came across.' His voice dropped, taking on a subtly dif-ferent note. 'And certainly the most interesting.'

Someone outside of herself asked the blunt question. 'Do you expect to have an affair with all your models, Dominic?'

He was in no way thrown. 'I expect nothing—rest easy. I think our table is ready.'

He kept the conversation on a strictly impersonal level during the meal, discussing photography from a profes-sional angle. Once or twice Sharon found her attention wandering from what he was saying in fascination with the total absorption in his face. Here was a man who obviously loved his job above all else. Perhaps it was the same commitment which had contributed towards the break-up of his marriage. Certainly no woman would want to take second place to a camera, even if she were on the other side of it. His wife had been a photographic model before her marriage, and still was now, although her heyday seemed to have passed. The top earning time for close-up work must be very short.

The studio was also Dominic's home address, the whole occupying the top floor of the building just off Kingsway. There were examples of his art everywhere, including several studies of his former wife.

'Good, aren't they?' Dominic commented casually, seeing her looking at the latter. 'Some of the best I ever did of her.'

'You don't mind the constant reminder?' Sharon asked, and he looked surprised.

'Why should I? We parted on reasonable terms.'

'A friendly divorce?'

'That's right. No use feeling bitter just because something didn't work out the way you imagined it might.' The pause was just long enough to lend weight. 'No use hanging on in the hope that it might improve either. The best you'll come up with is a compromise.'

'That's an improvement on stalemate, surely?'

'Not noticeably. The human mind doesn't adjust easily to compromise. We all want the ideal, and when we don't get it we start looking round for someone to blame. You haven't seen your own stuff yet.'

Sharon accepted the change of subject, following him round one of the screens dividing the huge studio into various areas, to give vent to a startled exclamation at the sight of her own face gazing back at her from every angle. There must be fifty or so different shots, she judged, although she didn't remember him taking as many. It was a little like standing in a hall of mirrors, some of them magnifying, others surely designed to add new dimensions to an expression. Was that really her face up there wearing the mysterious little Mona Lisa smile? And that one next to it, head thrown back, lips parted on a bubbling laugh it was almost possible to hear!

'Like them?' Dominic asked, watching her.

'Oh yes,' she said. 'But do I really look like that?'

He laughed. 'From that angle and with the light falling right and suitably primed with the right kind of thoughts, yes. The camera doesn't lie, it simply captures an instant in time. Your face is expressive when you're relaxed and off guard. I'll have to think of something to give you a smouldering look when the time comes.'

Sharon didn't turn her head. 'Why smouldering?'

'To suit the sexy siren type you'll be portraying among others. The idea is that Lucci cosmetics will enhance every occasion, make a woman feel the way she looks. You'll be seen in every possible situation from the seductive to the athletic. Even on a tennis court no woman who cares about herself should be without Lucci!'

'I don't play tennis,' she said, straightfaced, and Dominic reached out a fist to gently feint at the side of her jaw.

'Better watch that sense of humour. These people take their jobs very seriously, and they'll expect you to do the same. It's big money we're talking about.'

'Sorry.' She tried to look penitent and failed utterly because his own eyes were dancing too. The laughter died in them both as their glances locked and held. In that moment, Sharon knew she only had to make the slightest movement towards Dominic for him to take her in his arms. She took the step—away from him—and the moment was past, but not the emotion which had prompted the brief hesitation. She had wanted him to kiss her; she still wanted it. There were other men in the world apart from Lee.

Dominic made no attempt to press home an advantage he must have recognised. 'Come and have a drink,' he said. 'They'll be here soon.'

Seated in the artistically decorated and imaginatively furnished living room behind the studio, Sharon drank from the glass he gave her without having much idea what was in it. The elation had gone, leaving her flat. The whole idea was useless. She'd never make a model. She wasn't even sure she wanted to any more.

Dominic said nothing for a few minutes, just sat watching her, his own drink untouched. Finally he came over and took the glass from her, then sat down beside her on the long sofa and turned her towards him. There was determination written in his eyes.

'Sharon,' he said, 'you're going to make it. I won't let you let yourself down. If that husband of yours can't make you happy, ditch him.'

Her mouth twisted wryly. 'After three weeks?'

'Three weeks, three months—what difference is it going to make? You'll be independent after this.' He paused. 'If money's the problem I can arrange for an advance on your fee. I even know of an apartment you could rent. Friend of mine went to Spain last week for six-months. His lease allows him to arrange a sub-tenancy, and he asked me to do it for him. Just say the word.'

She shook her head. 'You're going too fast, Dominic. I can't make a decision like that in a few minutes.'

'Well then, think about it. But later. For now just concentrate on being what I tell you to be. Incidentally, you don't have to use the name Brent at all if you don't want to. What's your maiden name?'

He nodded when she told him. 'Good enough. It rolls off the tongue. Sharon Tiler it is.' He straightened as a bell rang faintly. 'That's them now. They're using the studio entrance.' His smile was reassuring. 'You look great!'

Roger Venables was a small, balding man around fifty, with a pair of the shrewdest eyes Sharon had ever encountered. The promotion's director more accurately fitted prior conceptions: tall, beautifully groomed and possessed of a businesslike manner which got straight to the matter in hand with an instruction to the accompanying cosmetician to start practising his profession.

Named Charles, the latter addressed Sharon with a cheerful familiarity sprinkled liberally with endearments.

'Love the hair,' he said. 'Beautiful colour! Natural, too, if I'm not out of my tiny mind? Sorry, darling, but I'm going to have to take all this off and start again from the bottom. We can't have a Lucci girl who isn't pure right through to the skin, can we, Roger dear?'

Roger dear grunted something unintelligible and went on discussing technicalities with Dominic and Lucy Wells. Aside from a nod on introduction, he had barely acknowledged Sharon's presence at all so far. Oddly enough, instead of unnerving her the indifference put her on her mettle. She might be just a canvas to him, but she had Dominic's assurance that she was the best one going for this particular job.

She was fascinated by the deft movements of the man working on her face, and only wished she could see what he was doing. Her face felt good when he had finished, skin supple and unclogged, lips smooth as silk. Perhaps the Lucci products did have special properties after all.

Lucy Wells came over to view her at closer quarters before calling on the managing director for an opinion. Lips pursed, she moved round Sharon like someone studying a piece of doubtful sculpture, expression giving no hint of her reactions.

'That's excellent, Charles,' she pronounced at length.

'Beautiful emphasis on the eyes! Roger, come and take a look.'

Roger came, took a look and nodded approval. 'How about movement? The TV outline calls for her to walk from the mirror to the door with the camera coming in on her face as she opens it. Can we try it?'

'Of course.' To Sharon she said briskly, 'Will you walk over there and open the door.'

Sharon did so, too angry to be nervous, stalking back to the little group again with expression controlled.

'That should do,' said Roger Venables. 'I'd have preferred a more stationary scene myself, but Bill assures me the public want a little action even in the adverts these days. So we go ahead. You know what's needed this end, Dominic. Give it all you've got.' Without glancing at Sharon again, he added, 'See to the contract, Lucy.'

Dominic gave a quick shake of his head as Sharon's came up, but she ignored the appeal. She said clearly, 'I'm not sure I want to do this job yet. I'd like time to think it over.'

She had their attention now—all of it. Only Charles appeared to find anything amusing in the situation. Lucy Wells was the first to speak.

'As a complete unknown you should be grateful for an opportunity like this one. The top professionals would give their eyeteeth for it!'

'Except that it isn't a well-known name you want,' Sharon came back, determined not to be put down. 'The Lucci girl has to be new to go with the product, doesn't she? If the public recognise the face it could detract from the impact.'

The older woman's eyes flickered. 'There are other possibilities apart from yourself.'

'But none quite right or you'd have settled for one of

them before this. And you don't have too much time left to start looking again.'

Roger Venables gave vent to a sudden, unexpected chuckle. 'She's got us over a barrel, Lucy, and she knows it.' For the first time he was looking at Sharon as one human being to another. 'How much time do you need?'

'Overnight,' she said.

'All right, you've got it. If you decide against it, let Dominic know and he'll just have to find us someone else.' From the tone of his voice he didn't believe that a very likely event. She was being indulged—allowed to get away with a capricious gesture purely because of the lack of time in which to find another suitable Lucci girl.

'Good for you, darling!' murmured Charles approvingly as he gathered up the case containing the tools of his trade to follow the others from the studio. 'Don't let them push you around! See you next week.'

Sharon met Dominic's eyes as the outer door closed behind the trio, and lifted her shoulders in a shrug that was half apologetic and half defiant.

'All right, say it?'

'Say what?' he countered. 'You judged the situation extremely well for a beginner. Not that many beginners would have the nerve to do what you just did.' He paused, studying her. 'Do you really need to make the decision, or were you simply making a point?'

'A little of both,' she admitted. 'I'm not sure, Dominic.'

'About the job itself, or how it's going to affect your marriage?' he asked bluntly. 'If you were so keen on preserving the last you wouldn't have involved yourself in the first. You'd have told me on the phone that you weren't interested.'

'I am interested. Who wouldn't be?' She made a small helpless gesture. 'I don't know why I'm hesitating. I don't even have a marriage to harm any more—Lee wants a separation as soon as he gets back.'

'Then give it to him. You don't need him.' Suddenly Dominic was across the intervening space and reaching for her, kissing her with a hunger which drew involuntary response from her. 'Don't go back,' he said on a rough note a moment or two later. 'Move in here with me.'

Still standing in the circle of his arms, Sharon gave a tiny sigh. 'Just like that?'

'No, not just like that. I haven't been able to get you out of my mind since the first day we met.' He put her a little way away from him to look down into her face, his own serious. 'Sharon, we both need somebody—not just professionally, but to be close to. I won't pretend I haven't looked at another girl since Caro and I broke up, but this it different. I could easily fall in love with you.' The ball of his thumb gently smoothed the line of her cheek down to the corner of her mouth. 'This face fascinates me. It's a photographer's dream—I want to catch its every mood!'

'If it hadn't been for the hairstyle, you'd never even have noticed me,' she sighed deprecatingly, and he smiled.

'If I'd got close enough I'd have noticed all right. Bone structure like yours can be blurred by the wrong outline, but it can't be totally hidden. What the hair does is make you stand out at first glance, that's all. The beauty would still be there even without it.'

She moved away from him, using humour to lighten the moment. 'Bald or not, I don't think I can accept your offer. If I'm going to do this job it has to be on a professional level.'

'Why?' he demanded. 'You're not in love with your husband.'

A shutter came down in her throat. 'That's why,' she said. 'I've already made one mistake, I don't want to make another. Attraction isn't enough, Dominic.'

It was a moment or two before he answered. Finally he sighed and shrugged resignedly. 'All right, if that's how it has to be. But you have to let me use you outside the Lucci contract as well. Is it a deal?'

There was no use in prolonging the decision; nothing was going to alter—overnight. Sharon nodded. 'It's a deal.'

'Good. I'll pass the news on in the morning. They want the still work out first before you're passed on to the filming crew. As to the other—Mind if we make a start now?'

'It's gone five,' she pointed out, aware of a sudden reluctance to linger.

'So we'll put in a couple of hours, then we'll have dinner and I'll drive you home.'

She didn't have a home, Sharon thought dully. It was only a place to stay until Lee came back.

The photographic session proved to be more tiring than she had allowed for. By a quarter to seven she was more than ready to call it a day.

'You'll have to acquire a little more stamina than this,' Dominic observed dryly, giving in to her entreaties in the end. 'It could take a whole morning to get exactly the right shot for just one Lucci spread, and they want a dozen different ones to start with.'

'Will Roger Venables and that woman be here while you're taking the photographs?' she asked on a note of doubt.

He shook his head. 'I don't like an audience when I work. It makes the model nervous and it makes me nervous. Charles will have to be around, of course, for any necessary touching up between times, but I don't think you'll find him any problem.'

'No,' she agreed. 'I rather liked Charles.'

'You mean you felt safe with him.'

A pang shot through her. 'That's the kind of remark I'd expect from Lee, not you.'

'Apparently we've more in common than you thought.' He caught her eye and made a wry gesture. 'Don't mind me. I guess I'm just not used to being turned down. There's a dressing room over in the corner if you want to tidy up before we go out.'

He was right, she thought, following his directions. He and Lee did have a lot in common. But at least Dominic could accept a refusal.

The dressing room was small but beautifully equipped. The mirror set into the wall over the dressing unit had bulbs round it in theatrical style, throwing the light where it was wanted directly on to the face. Seeing herself for the first time in professionally applied make-up, Sharon had to admit that the effect was indeed excellent. The shading over her eyes alone was a work of art, bringing out the blueness and making the whites sparkle without being in the least overdone.

She decided to leave well alone for the present, contenting herself with a token dab of compressed powder to remove the shine from her nose. Luckily it was roughly the same shade as the loose stuff Charles had used. No doubt the make-up for her tennis-playing shot would rely more on the healthy sheen imparted by a light foundation. Personally, she couldn't imagine anyone wanting to wear make-up at all to play tennis, but there must be plenty who did.

Sitting there in front of the mirror, she tried to think rationally about the coming weekend when Lee came home again. There had been no time for him to cancel the family party planned for Saturday night—unless he had done so early this morning, which seemed doubtful.

Surely he wouldn't expect to carry that through before going their separate ways? Where was the point?

Perhaps he expected her to cancel it in his absence considering what had passed between them. Yet why should she be subjected to the questioning certain to follow any such action? It was Lee's family; let him be the one to do the telling. The best thing she could do was simply not be there at White Ladies on Friday when he returned.

Emotions tightly under control, she went out to the studio again, passing from there through to the living room when she found it empty. An angled wooden stair-case at the far end led to an upper floor partitioned off from the lower only by sliding parchment screens. Dominic's voice came from behind these.

'Shan't be a tick—just getting changed. Help yourself to a drink.'

Sharon did so, splashing just enough gin into a glass of lime to taste.

'You don't have to take me out to dinner,' she called, holding the glass in her hand. 'I'm not all that hungry, as a matter of fact.'

'Well, I am,' he said, appearing at the top of the stairs buttoning the cuffs of a pale pink shirt. 'Anyway, I want to talk to you.'

'You can do that here.'

'Not without other interests getting in the way.' He gained the bottom step, slinging the wine-coloured corded jacket of his suit across a chair in passing as he came to mix himself a drink. 'What about that sub-tenancy?'

'Funny,' she said, 'that's just what I was going to ask you.' The hesitation was fleeting. 'Will I be able to afford it?'

'Adequately. You'd have found that out for yourself if you'd signed that contract this afternoon.'

Sharon ignored the last, drawing a long slow breath. 'Then I'll take it. Where is it, by the way?'

'Just around the corner. Fully furnished, of course. You won't need a thing apart from personal items. Treen's an artist, although he makes his living doing the commercial stuff mostly. You might find the decor a bit way out.'

'Treen?' she queried.

'That's his surname. Nobody ever calls him anything else, probably because of the way he slashes it across the foot of every piece of work he does. I'm not even sure of his initials, and I've known him three years.' He drained the glass and put it down with a small thud. 'I'll take you round there now and let you see the place.'

'No, not tonight.' Sharon could not have explained her reluctance. 'I'll move in on Friday, if that's all right.'

Dominic gave her a curious glance but refrained from comment. 'Fine. I'll give you the key and the address, then you can go straight in when you arrive. Shall we go and get that meal?'

In direct contrast to their lunchtime date, he chose to eat French cooking in an Art Nouveau setting which set Sharon's teeth on edge.

'Designed by David Hicks,' Dominic advised, noting her reaction. 'If you don't like this you won't like the apartment.'

'I'll learn to live with it,' she assured him. 'It can only be for six months anyway.'

'That's right. What will you do when Treen comes back?'

'Find somewhere else.' Sharon didn't want to think that far ahead. 'Always providing I'm still working.'

'You'll be working—I can guarantee that.'

'With you?'

'With Lucci. That's a two-year exclusive ownership

they're talking about. For anyone else to use you at the same time would ruin the whole idea.'

'You're doing it.'

'For my own satisfaction at the moment. Naturally I'll pay you top rate.'

She put out an impulsive hand to lightly cover his. 'I don't want paying, Dominic. I'm only too glad there's some way I can repay you for all you've done for me.'

Her glance slid away from the flicker in his, coming to rest on the face of the woman at the next table who was looking their way. Recognition was instant on Sharon's part, and must have revealed itself in her expression, for the other's uncertainty gave way to swift conviction.

'I've been wondering if it was you for the last fifteen minutes,' she said leaning closer to speak across Dominics shoulder. 'You look so different, darling! How's Lee? I thought you two were still in the South of France. Lora said you'd gone down there from Switzerland.'

'We got back last week.' Sharon kept her tone level with difficulty. If nothing else, she would have recognised the voice. Strange how distant the day of her wedding seemed now. She wasn't even the same person who had listened to that conversation down on the terrace. 'This is Dominic Foster. I'm afraid I don't remember your name.'

'Joyce Gregory.' The smile held a dangerous quality, the wave of her hand indicating her own escort who was looking distinctly uncomfortable. 'Peter Thornton— Sharon Brent, Peter, Lee's wife. You remember?' She cut through his mumbled reply, turning back to Dominic who had twisted round a little in his chair in polite response to the introductions. 'Not *the* Dominic Foster? Yes, of course it is! But how absolutely marvellous! I'm a great admirer of your work, Mr Foster. Imagine

Sharon knowing you. You weren't a model before you met Lee, were you, Sharon?'

'No,' she said with control.

Dominic took a hand in proceedings, obviously seeing no sense in beating about the bush. 'Sharon has a great future ahead of her. She's about to sign a contract that will put her straight into the top rank.'

'Really?' Joyce looked thoroughly taken aback and not a little envious. 'Well, congratulations! How does Lee feel about it? I'd have thought he'd have been here helping you celebrate.'

'He's in Copenhagen,' Sharon said. 'He doesn't know yet.'

'Oh dear,' came the wryly sympathetic response, totally belied by the malicious gleam in her eyes. 'I can't really see him liking the idea of a working wife.' Especially in this particular line of work, her tone implied. 'Still, I suppose he has to accept a *fait accompli*.'

The arrival of their own first course successfully drew her attention at that point. Catching Dominic's eyes, Sharon gave a small shake of her head in answer to the question plainly written there. To get up and leave now would give the woman even more fuel for the fire. She would know soon enough about the break-up of the Brent marriage. Until then let her make do with what gossip she already had.

Neither she nor Dominic enjoyed the meal when it came, even though Joyce said no more. Dominic asked for the bill with the coffee, he being the one to insist on leaving when the other two showed no sign of doing so.

'Going already?' asked their neighbour blithely when they got up. 'What a shame! I thought we might all have a drink together to round off the evening. Another time, perhaps. Regards to Lee!'

'Bitch,' Dominic said softly when they were outside in the blessedly fresh air.

Sharon felt surprisingly unmoved—or numb; she wasn't sure which. 'I don't suppose she can be blamed for thinking the worst. Here I am, not a month married, and holding hands with another man across an intimate table for two. It would take a saint to keep an open mind.'

'I'm not talking about that aspect. There was just no call for the innuendo.'

'I think she was more than interested in Lee herself,' Sharon said on a dull note. 'It put her nose out of joint when he married me instead. She should be highly delighted when the news filters through. She may even stand a chance of stepping into my shoes.'

'Not if this husband of yours has any sense.' Dominic opened the car door for her before adding, 'You're still set on leaving him, then?'

'There's no alternative,' she said, sliding into the seat. 'He wants it too.'

'You mean he said he does. We all have moments when we lash out with things we don't mean.'

She shook her head. 'It doesn't make any difference, Dominic. I can't go on living with him. Not now.'

He closed the door and came round to get in beside her, switching on the engine and leaving it to tick over for a moment as he turned his head to look at her.

'Sharon, if you feel like that why go back at all? You could move into the apartment tonight. I'll go out to the house in the morning to collect your things.'

Her smile was bleak. 'You wouldn't know what to bring, even if Mrs Reynolds would let you in the house. I don't want anything bought with Lee's money. He thinks that's all I married him for.'

'And it wasn't?'

'No. I was in love with him—about as far as he was in love with me. That was the trouble, we didn't know one another well enough for trust to have developed. It was all surface.'

'It often happens.' He put the car into drive and began edging out from the curb. 'I'll take you back.'

It was almost eleven-thirty when they eventually reached the house. Sharon forbore from asking Dominic to drop her at the bottom of the drive. Why should she care if Mrs Reynolds saw her get out of the car? Come Friday there would be little doubt left in her mind as to the situation.

'I can't ask you in,' she said apologetically. 'I don't feel I have the right any more.'

Dominic made no immediate answer. He was looking at the house outlined in bright moonlight, a wistful expression on his face. 'Beautiful proportions! Make a terrific setting for a couple of the Lucci shots. You don't suppose ...'

'No,' she said with sharpness, 'I don't. When I leave here on Friday I shan't be coming back—for any reason.'

'Too bad.' He turned his head. 'When do you expect to be in town? Time, I mean.'

'Morning definitely. Lee said he would be going straight in to the office, but he might just take it into his head to come home first.'

'You don't want me to come and fetch you?'

'No, I'll get a taxi.'

'No chauffeur-driven Rolls?'

'They went with Lee's father when he left. Lee prefers to drive himself.'

'Can't blame him for that. I had to have a driver once myself when I was banned for a year. Nearly drove me round the bend.' Dominic leaned over swiftly and kissed her hard on the lips before she could move. 'That's to remember me by. I don't despair of making you want more of the same some time.'

She watched the car vanish down the drive before going with reluctance indoors. Mrs Reynolds appeared from the rear premises as she mounted the stairs, looking up at her expressionlessly.

'Mr Brent phoned earlier. I told him you went to town.'

Sharon didn't turn her head, hand curved tightly over the polished banister. 'Did he say he'd phone again?'

'No, he didn't.' The other seemed to take a faint relish in saying it. 'About nine-thirty it was.'

Late enough for a husband to expect any wife to be sitting safely at home. Not that it made any difference. Nothing he could have had to say would change things between them. It was over.

CHAPTER EIGHT

It was round about noon on the Thursday when Sharon finally decided she had had enough. What she was afraid of more than anything else was a visit from Richard. There was no way she was going to be able to deceive him; he was too shrewd a judge for that.

With the decision made it suddenly became easier. The clothes she was taking with her were already sorted and only needing packing into two suitcases. She left the others without regret; they belonged to a part of her life she wanted to put right behind her.

It was Mrs Reynolds' day off, and the domestic help too had left. There was no one around to see the taxi she had ordered arrive, or her bags being loaded into it. The letter for Lee she left propped in a prominent position on the desk in the library where he couldn't fail to see it. If he did ring again tonight there would be no answer at all. Mrs Reynolds was visiting friends and would not be back herself before eleven.

Treen's flat was on the first floor. Sharon offered the taxi driver a lavish tip to carry her cases up for her, and closed the door on his departure with a sense of shutting out the world. The room facing her was large and airy, with two tall windows curtained in unbleached cotton letting in maximum light. The collection of tubular steel and glass furnishings left her cold, as did also the majority of the modern abstract paintings practically covering the whole of one wall. No particular furnishing style, she judged, but rather a combination of several. It was going to take some getting used to after White Ladies.

The bedroom had a huge mural decorating one wall, but there was plenty of storage space. It was still only a little after four when Sharon finished her unpacking. She was going to need certain essential items of food to carry her through till the next day when she could work out a proper list, she realised. Tomorrow also there was the contract to sign—and with luck an advance to collect. If she didn't get that she had no idea what she was going to do. But Dominic had assured her he could arrange it, she reminded herself. He would hardly have offered her the use of his friend's place had there been any doubt as to her ability to pay for it. Everything was going to be all right.

Everything? Depression swamped her suddenly. How

could everything be all right? She had left her husband after one short month of marriage. No matter what came after, that fact would always be with her.

The shopping didn't take long. Sharon stashed away the few items in the small kitchen, and without much interest decided to cook herself an omelette for tea. She ate only half of it before pushing it away, taking a second cup of coffee through to the living room to leaf through Treen's extensive collection of records and tapes. Her first choice filled the place with sound yet oddly seemed to emphasise the loneliness. She switched hurriedly to a quieter theme, lying back on a surprisingly comfortable if unconventionally shaped lounging chair to listen with closed eyes and a growing heaviness inside her.

She must have dozed at some point, coming awake with a jerk to find the tape finished and the remainder of her coffee skinned over in the cup. The sound which had woken her came again, louder and longer this time, as if whoever was outside the door was holding his or her finger on the bell.

Dominic, she thought foggily, struggling to her feet. It could only be Dominic. Perhaps he had brought the contract—or at least a copy of it so that she had time to read it through properly before signing it tomorrow.

It was only just beginning to penetrate the mists of sleep that Dominic didn't know she was here yet when she reached the door, and the sight of Lee standing there with a finger still outstretched to the bell came as a shock. She looked at him as one might at a ghost, every vestige of colour drained from her face.

He was dressed formally in a dark suit, which made the hint of five o'clock shadow along his jawline even more incongruous. The grey eyes were like chips of ice.

'What the devil are you playing at?' he demanded harshly.

Sharon pulled herself together with an effort. 'You'd better come in,' she said.

She stepped back as he did so, leaving him to close the door again. 'I wasn't expecting you back until tomorrow,' she stated stupidly.

'We finished early, so I caught the afternoon plane. Luckily I went to the library more or less as soon as I got in, or I'd still be in the dark.' He spoke on a clipped note which underlined the pent up anger. 'Whose place is this?'

'His name is Treen,' she told him. 'He's an artist.'

'He?'

'It's all right, I'm quite alone. He moved to Spain for six months.' Limbs unsteady, she indicated the nearest seat. 'Won't you sit down?'

'This isn't a social occasion,' Lee retorted grimly. 'I want this letter explaining. Who or what is Lucci?'

'It's a new line in cosmetics which is going to take the country by storm.' Her chin lifted. 'With a little assistance from me.'

'You don't have any modelling experience. You couldn't have walked into a job like that in a couple of days!'

'I didn't walk into it, I was drafted.' To Sharon the whole situation was fast taking on an element of ludicrousness. 'You've heard of Dominic Foster, the photographer? Well, I met him that afternoon in St Tropez. He offered me the job then, only I never believed he'd follow it through.'

'When did he?' The question was quiet, Lee's face suddenly wiped clean of expression. 'Was he the reason you found yourself needing to provoke a rift between us on Monday night?'

'A rift?' Her voice quivered at the memory. 'Don't try finding excuses for your own behaviour. There's no way you're ever going to justify what you did!'

'I'm not looking for justification. All I want is the truth. Were you planning on leaving even then?'

'No,' she said. 'It was Tuesday before Dominic contacted me. Not that it makes any real difference considering what you yourself said about obtaining a separation order when you got back.'

'That was said off the top, and you knew it.'

'No, I didn't know it!' Her voice had risen. 'Neither did you! You had time to think while you were away, didn't you, Lee? You still want that control, and you don't stand a chance if we break up? Well, it's too late, do you hear? It's just too late!'

'Is it?' he asked grimly, and reached for her.

At which point she stopped fighting him and began kissing him back, Sharon wasn't wholly certain. All she did know was the melting of anger into passion of another kind, the blotting out of all that had gone before in the overwhelming emotion of the moment. She had missed him so much; she hadn't known *how* much.

It was Lee himself who called a halt, holding her to him with his cheek resting against her temple, the sound of his breathing heavy in her ear.

'We have to talk,' he said on a far from level note. 'This only blurs the main issue. Sharon, how do you feel about starting again?'

She was silent for a long moment, hardly able to sort out what she felt about anything right then. 'From scratch?' she forced herself to ask at length.

'No, that isn't possible. I mean start again from here.' His hands were warm at her back. 'I've tried to convince myself that I'm better off without you, but it doesn't work. I want you more than I need my pride. Obviously you face the same difficulty. We can build something out of that, surely.' He held her a little away from him, searching her face with questioning eyes. 'Come back with me.'

Gazing back at him, Sharon felt her heart contract. He hadn't tried to pretend he loved her because it wouldn't be true—any more than it would be entirely true for her to say it either—yes, there was reason to hope that the feeling might develop given the time and opportunity.

'What about this contract with Lucci?' she asked, playing for a little of the former while knowing full well she was going to say yes come what may.

'Do it if you want to.'

'You wouldn't mind?'

The smile came wryly. 'It isn't a case of minding. I don't have the right to ask you to give it up.'

That admittance alone was worth a great deal, Sharon thought. She opened her mouth to reply and froze in surprise at the sound of a key being inserted in the outer lock, feeling Lee stiffen too. When Dominic walked into the flat they were standing like a pair of figures caught in suspended animation, heads turned towards him.

He was carrying a bunch of flowers wrapped in florist's paper, and still held the key dangling from the ring on his finger. His disconcertion on seeing them would have been comical under other circumstances.

'Sorry,' he said. 'I didn't know there was anyone here.'

'Obviously.' Lee's voice was low, the glance he gave Sharon as he abruptly released her smacking of bitter contempt. 'Spain, didn't you say?'

'This isn't Treen.' She was shaken by the swiftness of the change in him, voice taking on an edge. 'Don't jump to conclusions, Lee. I didn't know Dominic had a key to the apartment.'

'No, she didn't,' agreed the latter. 'I came round to make sure everything was okay for Sharon to move in tomorrow, which was the original arrangement. That's all there is to it.'

'He doesn't believe you,' Sharon said flatly. 'You're just wasting your breath, Dominic.'

'You're both wasting your breath,' came the hard retort. 'It won't be the first time you've been cited as co-respondent, will it, Foster?'

'Now wait a minute!' Dominic himself was angry now. 'You can't do me much harm, but Sharon is another matter.'

'You mean it might ruin her new career before it even gets started?' He was at the door now, hand already easing back the Yale lock. He didn't even look in Sharon's direction again. 'Too bad!'

Sharon drew in a deep shuddering breath as the door closed behind him. The whole episode had happened so fast; one minute they had been on the verge of a reconciliation, the next even further apart than before.

For a man of confidence, Dominic was looking singularly helpless. 'What can I say?' he asked. 'I'd no idea there was anyone in the flat. I was going to leave you the spare key along with the flowers.' He glanced at the latter wryly, and dropped them on a table. 'How about if I go after him and try to make him see reason?'

'No,' she said. 'It wouldn't work.'

The question was a moment or two in coming, his regard level on her face. 'Does it matter very much?'

Right at that moment nothing mattered. She felt utterly shorn of emotion.

'No,' she said again. 'Would you like some coffee now you're here? I'm afraid I haven't anything stronger.'

By common if unspoken consent, they shelved the whole subject for the present and concentrated on other matters. Dominic had brought along a copy of the contract Sharon was expected to sign the following day, and insisted on going through it with her.

'They're looking on you as my discovery,' he said. 'If anything goes wrong I'm going to carry the can. There are conditions attached to the contract to safeguard their interests. I took it on myself to accept them provisionally on your behalf, but you'll need to read them through yourself before you sign.' His tone altered a little. 'The one about adverse publicity might cause some trouble if that husband of yours does as he implied.'

'He won't.' She said it with flat conviction. 'There's no way his father is going to let the family name be dragged through the mud. If there's going to be a divorce it will be a quiet, uncontested one.'

'For which you're going to have to wait two years.' Dominic shrugged when she failed to respond. 'At least you're not going to run into any problems with condition number three.'

Sharon looked at it, and still felt nothing. The compilers were quite right : getting herself pregnant during the coming two years would ruin the whole show. Well, as Dominic had said, they didn't need to worry about that. They didn't need worry about anything. She was going to dedicate herself heart and soul to making a success of this job.

The signing session proved less of an ordeal than she had anticipated, the advance offered more than enough to set her mind at rest with regard to living expenses for a few months.

'We expect a lot from you for it,' said Lucy Wells with candour, handing over the cheque. 'Make sure any private life stays private, and we'll all be happy.'

'I feel a cheat,' Sharon confessed to Dominic later. 'They don't even know I'm married.'

'They know. I told them you were an independent,' he

assured her. 'Let's just hope you're right about your
father-in-law's reactions. You're so sure he can control
his son to that extent? From what little I saw of him,
he didn't strike me as a man who'd please anybody but
himself.'

'It will pay him to in this case.' Her tone was emotion-
less. 'In fact, he could finish up with everything he ever
really wanted.' She changed the subject. 'When do we
start work?'

'Tuesday,' he said. 'We'll get the location work out of
the way first. They want authentic background detail, no
mock-ups. Hope your passport isn't due to run out or
anything.'

She was startled. 'We're going abroad?'

'Morocco. One line of the Lucci range is specially
formulated for hotter climates.' His mouth turned down
at the corner. 'Don't look so concerned. We'll have friend
Charles with us.'

It wasn't that particular aspect which was causing
the concern, but Sharon refrained from saying so. It was
too late now to start backing out. She was committed. If
Lee wanted to get in touch with her it would have to be
either before she went or when she got back. Not that
it would be a personal contact, she was certain. He
would simply instruct a solicitor to set the wheels in
motion. She only wished this deadness would lift. Any
kind of feeling at all was preferable to none.

It was Richard Brent who did the contacting in the
end. Opening the door to him on the Sunday afternoon
was somehow no surprise.

'I wasn't sure I'd find you in if I left it till this evening,'
he said.

Or alone if he had come this morning, Sharon sur-
mised, and was immediately ashamed of the uncharitable

thought. Richard had shown her nothing but kindness throughout their short acquaintance.

'Did Lee send you?' she asked, inviting him to a seat.

'You should know better than that. Lee wouldn't thank anybody for interfering in his affairs.'

She said bluntly, 'Then why are you?'

'Because I refuse to sit by and let the two of you make a total mess of your lives out of sheer muleheadedness! I managed to get your whereabouts out of him, but not the reason why you left.' He paused, the grey eyes, so like those of his son, searching her face. 'Sharon, surely nothing you can find to quarrel about after one month of marriage calls for such drastic action?'

She lifted her shoulders. 'At the time it seemed the only course of action.'

'Another woman?' The words were clipped.

'Not another woman,' she said. 'A girl. The one Lee thought I was when he married me.'

'I don't understand.' Richard looked genuinely perplexed. 'What are you talking about?'

'It would take too long to explain,' she sighed.

'I don't care how long it takes. Just tell me.'

Sharon gazed at him for a long moment, aware of the need growing inside her. To let go and confide in someone would be such a relief, yet was Lee's father the right person?

'I won't act on it,' he assured her, sensing her hesitation. 'Whatever the problem is it will be just between the two of us.'

Without coming to any conscious decision, she began to talk, feeling the floodgates open as all the pent-up misery of the last month came rushing out. She held little back, and made no attempt whatsoever to mitigate her own behaviour, beginning to see things clearly for the first time.

It was impossible to tell Richard's reactions from his expression: the ability to conceal emotion was another trait he shared with his son. When she finally trailed off into silence he made no comment for a moment or two, just sat there with that same contemplative regard.

'Say something,' she begged. 'What are you thinking?'

'I was thinking,' he said on a measured note, 'that neither of my offspring have anything to be proud of in themselves. Perhaps you can lay the blame for that at mine and Lorna's door. Tolerance and understanding are taught by example.'

'I'm as much to blame as anyone,' Sharon claimed. 'I should have given Lee a chance.'

'Yes, you should, but few of us act the way we should in moments of stress. You were hurt and you wanted to hurt back. That's understandable.'

She said swiftly, 'The same would apply to Lee,' and drew a wintry smile.

'You're defending him—that's a good sign. Not that I agree with you. Lee was well aware how unsure of yourself you were. If he'd handled the situation the right way he could have convinced you. However, that's by the way; it's here and now that we have to think about.' He paused. 'What do you feel about Lee now, Sharon? Be honest.'

'I'm not sure,' she confessed. 'I'm honestly not sure. I don't think I ever was. Perhaps I was telling a subconscious truth when I said I'd married him for money.'

Richard shook his head. 'I don't believe that—at least not wholly. The way you looked that very first day when I asked you if you loved him, that wasn't assumed. And you said only a few minutes ago that you were ready to agree to go back to him when your photographer friend burst in on you.'

'Ready to try again,' she corrected.

'All right, so try again. Let me take you out to White Ladies right now. I know he's home, I telephoned him just before coming round here.'

'He won't believe me,' she said tonelessly. 'About Dominic, I mean. Anyway, it's too late. I signed a two-year contract.'

'Contracts can be broken. I'll settle with these Lucci people if you'll just do as I ask.'

Sharon's jaw clenched. 'I'm sorry, but I won't go and plead with him. If he wants to see me, he knows where I am.'

'He already sank his pride the other night, according to what you've told me.' Richard's tone was gentle. 'And you have to admit, he had some cause for jumping to the wrong conclusion. If you showed yourself willing to make the same effort I think he'd believe you.' He gave a small sigh when she failed to respond. 'That's it, then. There's nothing more I can do.'

Sharon watched him get to his feet, an aching dryness in her throat. 'Shall you be delegating control of the Company to Lee?' she asked because she couldn't help herself, 'or to his cousin?'

His smile held irony. 'Don't let it worry you. You'll receive half of whatever price the house fetches on the market, of course, but not for some time. If you need money in the meantime ...'

'I don't.' The ache had become a lump, hard and un-yielding. 'Neither do I want anything out of White Ladies.'

'You're entitled to fifty per cent—I had both your names put on the deeds. Anyway, Lee won't want to live there on his own. He'll probably move back to the Grosvenor apartment.'

'If my name is on the deeds, he can't sell without my

consent,' she said fiercely. 'And I don't give it. You can tell him that!'

'I'll tell him. What he does about it is his own affair.' The glance he sent over her was harder. 'I don't think you know what you do want, Sharon, but you're going to have to decide. This life you're going to be leading may seem very glamorous and exciting on the surface, but there'll be times when you'll find it just as boring and tiring and downright frustrating as any other job. Two years is a long time to be tied.'

Not as long as a lifetime, Sharon reflected as the door closed behind him. In two years she could be free of all ties. Free to start her life again. It was a goal to aim for.

That goal seemed to recede over the following weeks rather than grow any nearer. Travelling was little pleasure, Sharon found, when the sole purpose was work. Rabat, Athens, Madrid; staying nowhere longer than forty-eight hours, and seeing nothing beyond the hotel and the spots Dominic chose for background; sweltering under a hot sun while the latter studied angle and light and Charles hovered anxiously in dread of a bead of perspiration ruining the satin perfection of his efforts.

Back in England, she learned to water-ski in the Lake District, to ride a horse; to hold a tennis raquet in a manner which at least suggested a degree of expertise. Of the three she preferred the riding, attaining enough proficiency to accompany Dominic on an early morning ride the day they were due to return to London.

'You'll soon have all sorts of strings to your bow,' he said, watching her dismount on their return to the stables. 'You should keep this one up. You've all the makings of a good horsewoman.'

'Trotting down Rotten Row on a Sunday morning?'

she responded wryly as they made their way to the car. 'Not quite the same, is it?'

'There are plenty of good places within easy reach. I'll introduce you to my particular weekend haunt at the first opportunity.'

Sharon glanced at him. 'Are we going to be very tied up when we get back to town?'

'For a few days while I complete the studio work, yes. Then you have the TV commercial to do—another day —and after that a nice long rest before you're needed again.'

'Doing what?'

'Anything you like—within the limits of your contract.' He paused, fingers ready to turn on the ignition. 'I've a job to cover in Edinburgh as soon as I'm through with the Lucci stuff, but there's nothing else so urgent it can't be left till the end of the month. How about the two of us taking a rest together? I'll even promise to leave my cameras behind.'

She kept her tone light. 'No strings attached?'

'Yes, there'll be strings attached. I'm not geared to platonic relationships.' The glance he gave her was purposeful. 'Sharon, you can't spend the next couple of years waiting for a divorce to come through. Neither can I, if it comes to that. Even if you had your freedom now I doubt if you'd be prepared to leap into marriage in a hurry again.'

'No,' she agreed, 'I wouldn't.'

'Then why not spend some time getting to know someone well enough to be sure of your feelings—and his? If we were still together after two years I'd say we stood a fair chance of making a go of it.'

She looked at him without expression. 'I'm not in love with you, Dominic.'

'I know that. It's a vastly overrated expression anyway.

Getting along together is more important—outside of the physical element, of course.'

'Oh, yes, we mustn't forget the physical element.'

His shrug was goodhumoured. 'If it's a monk you're after try a monastery.' He turned the key. 'We're going to have to get a move on if we're to make that train.'

There was no communication, personal or otherwise, from Lee over the next week or so. Dominic left for Edinburgh the day after Sharon finished the TV filming, promising to be back by the following weekend. Deprived of the anodyne work had provided, she found time dragging by on leaden wings and her thoughts turning more and more to the man whose name she still bore. The temptation to pick up the phone and dial White Ladies just to hear his voice became almost unbearable at times. Only the probability that it would be Mrs Reynolds who got to it first kept her from giving in to that particular need. What would it gain her, in any case? There could be no going back.

Nausea had hit her on three consecutive mornings before she could bring herself to acknowledge facts. Leaning wanly against the bathroom basin, she viewed her pale face with an edge of despair at the prospect facing her. At the very outside, she could be no more than six weeks gone, so nothing was likely to show for some time yet, but she could hardly go on concealing it indefinitely. What would happen to her job when the truth became obvious?

It was some moments before the longer-term prospect hit her. She was going to have a child : Lee's child. A new sensation crept into her, warm and soft. Ridiculously she put her fingers flat against her stomach, trying to feel any minute difference. Lee's child. Dark-haired like its father, blue-eyed like her : a pretty little girl, or a handsome little boy? There were supposed to be ways of telling the sex of a child before birth.

Realisation brought her down to earth again with a jerk. Lee's child, yes, but was he going to believe it? And even if he did, what did they do about it? It wasn't unknown for people to stay together purely for the sake of any children, only that was surely when the children were already born—old enough to be aware of having two parents to start with. There were plenty of one-parent families around these days. Some women even chose to have a child without taking a husband first because that was the only aspect of marriage they were interested in.

Yes, but how did they live? Maintenance from the father, if they were fortunate enough; social security if they were not. If Lee had enough conviction of parenthood to be willing to maintain the child, he would certainly not be agreeable to doing so from a distance. And he had to be convinced, didn't he? The time element saw to that. He had known she was a virgin that first night he had made love to her; he couldn't fail to have known. He might even be prepared to put their differences to one side in the light of this new development and take her back. Except that she didn't want to go back. Not on that footing.

She was going round in circles, Sharon thought wearily. She wasn't even completely certain she was pregnant at all yet. She would have to see a doctor and get confirmation before she started driving herself crazy worrying about the future.

Friday brought a totally unexpected visitor in the shape of Lee's sister Lora. Too stunned to be polite, Sharon could only stand in the doorway and gaze at the beautifully dressed and groomed figure of her sister-in-law. The other girl looked back at her coolly enough, yet there was a hint of something less than certainty in her eyes.

'I'm here at Daddy's suggestion,' she said, and allowed herself a faint smile. 'Or perhaps orders might be a better way of putting it. May I come in?'

'Yes, of course.' Sharon opened the door wider, trying to appear as composed and wishing she had taken the trouble to change into something a little more relaxing when she got in. 'It's a good thing you didn't come any earlier,' she tagged on jerkily. 'I only just got back myself a little while ago.'

'Yes, it seemed a good time. I'm on my way to meet Jason, so I mustn't be long.' Lora's glance went round the room, her nose wrinkling. 'Do you really like this sort of thing?'

'No,' said Sharon. 'It's somewhere to live.'

'A very expensive somewhere, I imagine, in this area.' Lora's eyes came back to Sharon's face and seemed suddenly to narrow a little. 'I hear you're doing some modelling. For Dominic Foster, no less!'

'He's doing the photographing, my contract is with the cosmetics company itself.' There was a brief pause before she added levelly, 'Lora, why are you here?'

The laugh held a wry note. 'The moment of truth! Apparently I'm the direct cause of you and Lee breaking up the way you did. I only hope you don't imagine I'd have said what I did to Joyce if I'd known you were in earshot.'

'I never thought about it,' Sharon confessed. 'Anyway, that wasn't the direct cause, only a contributory factor. I should never have married Lee—you were right about that. I didn't fit in with the Brent family ideals.'

'We're not a family—not a proper one. We never were. Mummy's an incurable snob, and according to Daddy

I'm well on the way to being the same.' Lora pulled a face. 'He's right, of course. I wanted Lee to marry somebody out of our own circle, somebody I'd be on a wavelength with.'

'Like Joyce Gregory, for instance?'

'Lord no! She'd have been my last choice. I suppose that's why I took such a delight in rubbing it in that she'd been passed over.' She paused. 'Mind if I sit down for a few minutes?'

'I'm so sorry, please do,' Sharon said ruefully. 'Can I get you something to drink?'

'No alcohol, thanks. I'm off it at present. I wouldn't say no to tea.'

'I'll make some. It won't take long.'

She prepared the tray like an automaton out in the kitchen, mind taken over by the conversation of the last few minutes. Not that anything Lora had said made any appreciable difference to the situation. She still had the same problem to face. The gynaecologist she had visited this afternoon had confirmed her own diagnosis and suggested she see her doctor at the earliest convenience. Despite the evidence of the wedding ring she had donned again especially for the occasion, it had been obvious that he suspected her actual status. She had found him sympathetic and understanding in a way which more than made up for that assessment.

What she now had to decide was what to do about it. Lee hadn't contacted her in almost a month. To phone him and make a bald announcement was out of the question. How did you tell a man you were separated from that you were going to have his child? It was something she was going to have to think about very, very carefully. Meanwhile she would just have to live with the blind misery which kept threatening to overtake her.

Lora was leafing through the portfolio of photographs

Dominic had left with her for idle perusal when she went back into the living room.

'Hope you don't mind,' the other said. 'I couldn't resist taking a peep. These really are superb! You look as if you'd been doing this kind of work all your life.'

'Thanks.' Sharon could not deny the pleasure in hearing the words. 'They're only copies, of course. The originals are with Lucci.'

'When is the campaign due to take off?'

'Next week.'

'So we'll be seeing these splashed across magazines and billboards.'

'Not all of them. I'm not sure myself which they've chosen yet.' She kept her tone level. 'There's also the TV commercial. Still, few of the people you and Lee know are likely to recognise me.'

Lora ignored the innuendo. 'That's true. You've changed out of all recognition.' Her eyes came up to study Sharon's face at closer quarters as the latter brought across her tea, the expression in them thoughtful. 'Not just outwardly either. Are you well, Sharon?'

'Of course.' The response was a mite too sharp. She attempted to soften it. 'A bit tired, perhaps. It's harder work than you'd imagine.'

The pause was lengthy. Lora was the first to break it. 'Who's responsible?' she asked. 'Lee, or Dominic Foster?'

Sharon's cup rattled sharply in its saucer as she reached out to put it down. 'I think you'd better go!'

'Because I took too good a guess? If it is Lee's he has a right to know.'

Denials were useless; somehow Sharon accepted that. She looked at her sister-in-law helplessly. 'How did you guess? It was only confirmed this afternoon.'

'Call it feminine intuition—plus a little practical ex-

perience. I've seen that particular look you have before
—namely through a mirror. It's quite a feeling, isn't it?
All that going on inside.'

'You mean you're expecting a baby too?'

'Not by intention—at least, not originally by intention.
One of those percentage accidents. Once I'd got over the
initial shock I found I quite liked the idea after all.
Jason, of course, is highly delighted.' Lora gave a faint
smile. 'In fact, I wouldn't put it past him to have indulged
in a little sabotage. He always said the time to have
children is while you're young enough to enjoy them. I
was the one who wanted to wait a few years.' The smile
vanished. 'You still haven't answered the question.'

Sharon brought up her head. 'It's Lee's.'

'Are you sure?'

'Quite sure. It couldn't be anyone else's. And you can
believe that or not, just as you like!'

'Don't jump down my throat—I believe you.' Lora's
tone was mild. 'Whether Lee will is another matter.'

'You're going to tell him?'

'Weren't you?'

Sharon sighed. 'I suppose eventually I'd have to. As
you say, he has a right to know.'

Lora studied her for a moment. 'Would you go back
to him?'

She shook her head, chest tight. 'I'm not sure I could.
Not just for that reason. Even if he wanted it.'

'Bringing up a child on your own wouldn't be easy.'

'I know.'

Something flickered in Lora's eyes. 'It doesn't leave
you with many alternatives.' She came to her feet, her
tea barely tasted. 'I have to go, I'm going to be late. Lee's
in Germany and not due back till next week. You realise
I'm going to have to tell him at first opportunity?'

'Yes.' Sharon rose too, acknowledging the lack of

sense in asking her to leave things a little longer. The sooner Lee knew, the sooner she would know his re-action. Until that moment there was little point in planning anything.

CHAPTER NINE

DOMINIC arrived back on the Saturday afternoon, taking time out only to dump his gear at his own place before coming round to see Sharon.

'All finished,' he announced triumphantly, swinging her up to press a kiss on her lips the moment she opened the door. 'I'm a free agent for the next five days. Where would you like to go? Somewhere we can watch your TV debut, of course. Can't miss that!' He saw her face clearly for the first time as he set her back on her feet, his own sobering suddenly. 'What happened?'

'You'd better sit down,' said Sharon. 'I have something to tell you.'

Dominic made no effort to comply, eyes fixed on her. 'So tell me.'

There was only one way to say it, and that was plainly. 'I'm pregnant.'

For a long moment Dominic failed to react in any way, face quite blank. When he did finally speak it was with control. 'How long?'

'Six weeks.'

'I meant how long have you known.'

'For certain, only since yesterday.'

'And before that?'

'Only two or three days. I . . .' She stopped, flushing a little at the meaningful lift of his eyebrow. 'All right, so I should have suspected it earlier than this. Perhaps I had too much on my mind.'

'Signing that contract should have jolted your memory,' he said. 'You must have known the possibility existed.'

'It just never occurred to me.' Her voice was ragged. 'I can't explain why. It simply didn't.'

'Or you deliberately ignored the risk in order to secure the job.'

'No! I wouldn't have done that!'

'It's what others are going to believe. It's too late now to stop the sales campaign and start over again. Everything is geared to it. What they're going to be stuck with is a change of image in mid-stream if you go ahead and have this baby.'

She stared at him, breath catching in her throat. 'What do you mean, *if* I have it?'

'There are other solutions. At six weeks there shouldn't be any problem.'

Teeth clenched, she said, 'There's no way I'd do what you're suggesting, Dominic, contract or no contract! They'll just have to find someone else to take my place. I never could see why it was so important to use the same person all the way through.'

'Advertising psychology. Yours not to reason why.' He spread his hands in a gesture of appeal. 'Sharon, you have to see sense. You'll not only be ruining your whole career, you'll be saddling yourself for life. I take it your husband doesn't know.'

'Not yet, but he will. His sister was here yesterday.'

'And you told her?'

'She guessed—she's pregnant herself. Apparently she

sensed the vibrations.' Her mouth felt stiff. 'I don't know what Lee will want to do about it. I don't know that he'll want to do anything about it outside what the law demands. One thing I am sure of, though, he'd never ask me to do what you just asked.'

'I was thinking of you as well as the Lucci job,' he protested swiftly. 'And what about us? What about the plans we made?'

'The plans *you* made. I never said I'd go along with them.'

'You encouraged me—made out you felt something for me.'

She said quietly, 'I did feel something for you Dominic. I liked you and I trusted you. I'm sorry if you're going to lose out on the Lucci contract because of me, but you're too big for it to make so much difference.'

'I shan't lose out at all.' His tone was cool. 'My responsibility only extends as far as making sure you lived up to my promises on the technical side, which I did. Your personal life was your own responsibility. They're not going to like being let down.'

'So let them sue me.'

'They might just do that.' He moved back to the door, turning to give her a final glance, mouth set on a line of regret. 'I think you're being a little fool, Sharon, but it's your funeral. If you change your mind you know where I am.'

Loneliness engulfed her the moment the door closed behind him. Lee wouldn't be back for several days and it was hardly likely that Lora would visit her again. What did she do with herself in all that time? For a moment she considered contacting Maureen at the office, but rejected the idea almost at once. There would be too many questions to evade. She was on her own and she must stay that way until this whole affair was settled one way or another.

The weekend dragged by. Sunday was fine and hot. Mindful of the need for fresh air and exercise, Sharon took a bus out to Hampstead Heath and went for a long walk, finishing up with tea at a well populated little café in Highgate Village. Everyone else she had seen that afternoon seemed to have been in family groups or at least pairs. She felt like an outcast.

The thought of the life stirring inside her was her only comfort. She clung to it fiercely. Lora had pointed out how difficult it would be to bring up a child on her own, but if Lee refused to acknowledge his responsibility, that was what she was going to do. She would manage somehow. As for the Lucci contract—well they couldn't get blood out of a stone. She would pay them back what she had left out of the advance and they'd have to whistle for the rest. In any case, she merited some payment for the work she had already put in.

It was with reluctance that she finally retraced her steps homeward. The sight of the silver Mercedes parked outside the building jerked her heart into her throat. No part of her was prepared for confrontation without warning like this. She had not anticipated an early return.

Lee was sitting in the car waiting for her. He got out when he saw her coming, eyes piercing through her.

'Where have you been?' he demanded without any kind of prior greeting. 'I've been here two hours.'

'I went for a walk,' she said, gathering herself together. 'I didn't expect you today. Lora said you weren't due back from Germany until the middle of the week.'

'Lora contacted me this morning.' His tone was a little less abrupt this time. 'Apparently she spent all yesterday worrying herself sick about you.'

'She shouldn't have done that. She has herself to think about.'

'Except that she isn't in the same position.' He moved away from the car door. 'We'd better go inside. We can't discuss something like this on a street corner.'

The apartment had never looked less welcoming, but Lee didn't even spare a glance around it. 'You'd better sit down,' he said. 'You look tired.'

'I'm not an invalid,' Sharon protested mildly, obeying. 'I feel perfectly fit.'

He didn't answer for a moment, just stood there looking at her with unreadable expression.

'Have you been to see anyone yet?' he asked at length.

'You mean a doctor?' She shook her head. 'Only the gynaecologist who confirmed it for me. He said to get in touch with my own G.P., but I don't have one at the moment. I was going to see about it this week.'

The following question was harsher. 'Does Foster know?'

'Yes.'

His lips thinned. 'I see.'

'No, you don't see,' Sharon said fiercely, sensing his assumption. 'I didn't tell him because he had a right to know. It ... just worked out that way. Dominic isn't the father, Lee—you are.'

There was no change in his expression. 'How can you be so sure?'

She had been expecting it, but it still hurt. Her eyes were bright, sparkling blue. 'Because you're the only man who ever had me, to put it in language you might understand! And if you don't want to believe that you'd better leave right now!'

His gaze didn't waver. 'He had a key to this place.'

'Which he left here, just as he told you he intended to do. The whole mix-up was my fault for moving in early.'

'You should never have moved in at all. We could have straightened things out if you hadn't been so eager to take that damned job!'

'It didn't seem so at the time.' Sharon spread her hands, looking up at the hard hewn features with appeal. 'Lee, what's the use in going over and over old ground? I left you because I thought it was what you wanted. The Lucci job was just a small part of it. It's over now anyway.' She paused unhappily. 'At least, the job is. I signed a contract which included a condition that I didn't get myself pregnant for two years. Dominic thinks they might sue.'

'They can try, I doubt if they'd get very far. They might be due to some compensation for non-completion. I'll put the Company's lawyers on to it.' He was speaking levelly, without emotion. 'When does the actual campaign get off the ground?'

'Wednesday. It's too late to get it stopped, if that's what you're thinking.'

'You're probably right. We'll just have to let it go. Get your things together, I'm taking you back to White Ladies.'

'Not like this,' said Sharon. She felt heartsick but resolute. 'It's no solution, Lee.'

'You don't have any choice. That's my child you're carrying, and you're coming home.'

She looked at him long and hard, trying to read the mind behind the grey eyes. 'You're quite sure about it? I don't want any half-truths. You have to be absolutely *sure*!'

'I'm sure.' For the first time the hardness relaxed a little. 'Lora almost had me convinced on the phone this morning. You made quite an impression on her the other day. She regrets not having taken the trouble to know you better before we were married.'

'She wouldn't have found the same person, though, would she.' It was a statement, not a question. 'I've changed considerably since then.' Her smile was bleak. 'If only I hadn't . . .'

'Stop that,' Lee cut in. 'We can't go back, so there's no use in wishing—you said it yourself not a few minutes ago. If we make it at all, we make it from here. Come on, I'll help you pack. I'll sort things out here later.'

Sharon took the hand he held out to assist her to her feet, feeling its firmness and strength with a surge of emotion. She wanted badly to feel his arms about her, but it was too soon for that. They had a long uphill climb ahead of them.

They were in the car and heading out of the city before she found the courage to say what was on her mind.

'If this hadn't happened, would you have gone on ignoring me?' she asked softly without turning her head towards him. 'It's been such a long time, Lee.'

'I honestly don't know,' he returned after a moment. 'I've been living from day to day. Work is a great panacea.'

And other women? she wondered, but refrained from voicing the question. If there had been anyone else while she had been away from him she had only herself to blame. 'You didn't attempt to start selling the house?' she asked instead.

'Without your permission?' It was the first hint of humour he had shown all evening, and encouraging. 'Eventually I'd have had to do something about it— about everything, I suppose.'

'You knew your father had been to see me.'

'He told me. He said you were no more capable of reasoned behaviour than I was.' The smile came again faintly. 'We're going to find ourselves watched with a gimlet eye for any signs of another break-up, especially in the circumstances.' He paused there, tone changing. 'You know, I still can't quite take it in.'

Sharon's heart jolted. 'You said you believed me.'

'I do. I wasn't talking about that. It's the very thought of it.' His glance slid sideways over her, as they came to a halt at some traffic lights. 'Apart from the tiredness you don't look any different.'

'It's only six weeks. It's too soon to be looking any different.'

'Except to another woman. Lora had the impression you wouldn't have said a word if she hadn't guessed. Did that include me too?'

Something in his voice drew her eyes to him. 'What are you trying to say?'

The hesitation was brief. 'She thought you might be tempted to do something drastic, the way things were— that's why she phoned me. I took the first available flight.'

'You must be tired yourself,' she murmured, and drew a sharpened glance.

'Don't avoid the question, Sharon. Did you consider getting rid of the baby?'

'No,' she said, 'not for a single minute. If you hadn't accepted it I'd have managed somehow.'

'Did you think there was any doubt?'

'If you believed it wasn't yours, yes. I can't see you taking on another man's child.'

He didn't attempt to deny the fact. 'You'd still have been my wife. I'd have made sure you got through.'

'Except that I wouldn't have accepted any help from you under those circumstances.' She stirred restlessly in her seat. 'Lee, you only have to work out the dates. You know when it happened as well as I do.'

He shook his head. 'I'm not doubting you. Not any more. Dad was right when he said I was judging you by my own moral standards.'

'Plus some fairly substantial evidence!'

'No excuse, but thanks anyway.'

They drove in silence for a distance after that, the car filled with the soft golden light of a magnificent sunset, the passing scenery still unfamiliar to Sharon. She had lived too short a time at White Ladies to think of it yet as home, but looked forward to seeing the lovely house again. There was only one real cloud on the scene.

She had said it before she was fully aware of the intention forming in her mind. 'Do you think it might be possible to get rid of Mrs Reynolds? I can't stand the woman.'

'It's done,' Lee said without turning a hair. 'We had a rather gritty exchange a couple of weeks ago, and she gave in her notice on the spot. I gave her six months' salary in lieu of notice and despatched her forthwith, as the saying goes. I've been leaving the domestic help to organise themselves since, but I can't say it's worked out so well.'

The relief was sweet. 'I can cope. I'll enjoy it.'

'Only until we find someone suitable. You're going to have other things to think about.'

She laughed, a sudden shaft of happiness flooding through her. 'How do you think other women cope?'

'I don't much care,' he said. 'You're not doing it. Tomorrow you're going to see Ian Anderson, our family doctor, and make sure everything is as it should be. All right?'

'Of course.' Sharon closed her eyes, ostensibly against the glare from the sun, aware that they still had a long way to go before she could safely give way to the emotions welling up inside her. Lee could be so wonderfully nice when he wanted to be. That question at the end was his way of stepping down a little, relinquishing total control. Not that he would expect anything but compliance with what he'd been saying regardless, she acknowledged with wry humour. He was too accustomed to organising.

The house was just as she remembered it, the last rays of sunlight catching the west windows. Inside was the same beautiful polished floor stretching away to the staircase, but no flowers to brighten the panelling and lend an air of welcome. First job tomorrow, Sharon promised herself, and felt the same warm glow at the knowledge that she would be here tomorrow.

Lee came in behind her carrying both her suitcases. 'I'll bring mine in later,' he said. 'These weigh a ton. Considering the amount of stuff you left behind, I'm surprised you could find enough to fill both of them.'

Sharon followed him up the stairs, eyes devouring the breadth of his shoulders, the leanness of his hips, remembering how it felt to run her fingers down over the smooth muscularity of his back and wanting him with a sudden desperate yearning.

'I bought some things overseas,' she said on a husky note because she had to say something. 'A lot I won't need now, of course.'

Lee waited until they were in the bedroom they had shared before responding, dropping both suitcases to the floor and turning to look at her with veiled grey eyes. 'Are you going to miss it?'

She shook her head, conscious of the double bed behind him and wishing he would swing her up and put her on it; merge the past into the present in the only way possible. The longing made her voice quiver a little. 'I shan't miss it at all. It wasn't what I wanted.'

He was still for a long moment, then made an abrupt movement, but it was towards the door, not her. 'I'll fetch my own things in and put the car away,' he said. 'Get a good night's sleep. I'll see you in the morning.'

Listening to the receding sound of his footsteps, Sharon wondered achingly if this was what was called poetic justice. Lee had brought her back home, had accepted his responsibilities, but he no longer wanted her. He couldn't have made that plainer. What kind of future was there for them now?

It was a question she was to ask herself many times over the following days. Lee was kindness itself, but the gulf remained. Doctor Anderson was a man about Richard Brent's age, and coming close to his own retirement date, as he admitted with obviously mixed feelings on the subject. He pronounced Sharon fit enough in the physical sense but prescribed a course of iron tablets to build up her vitality.

'At three months you'll start feeling much more yourself again,' he told her. 'By then the hormones have made their main adjustment and settled down again. Until then try not to let things worry you too much. You're a healthy young woman, there's no reason at all why you shouldn't have a fine bouncing baby.' His eyes twinkled behind their black-framed spectacles. 'And no reason at all why you shouldn't enjoy life to the full in the meantime.'

Sharon murmured some appropriate reply, hoping he would not see fit to impart the same advice to Lee at any time. The sensible thing might have been to reveal the true cause of her lack of vitality to the doctor, but he was too close to the family to run the risk. She had to see it through on her own.

Wednesday saw the initiation of the Lucci campaign with national coverage. Looking at the full-page spread in the magazine she had delivered weekly, Sharon felt oddly detached, as if the face looking back at her belonged to someone else entirely. Had she ever really been as blissfully happy as the picture made her appear? What was it Dominic had been saying to her to put that sparkle in her eyes, that warmth in her smile?

She watched Lee's face with some trepidation as he viewed the advertisement, aware that he would have paid anything asked to kill the campaign had it only been possible. It was impossible to tell what he was really thinking when he handed the magazine back to her. Certainly his smile nowhere reached his eyes.

'I'm not surprised they're so concerned about losing you,' was his own comment.

The evening was worse because it caught them relatively unawares in the middle of a play they had both wanted to watch. Seeing herself move across the screen was almost an embarrassment. Sharon wanted to cover her face with her fingers and shut out the sight of that other self looking so yearningly into the face of the man whose back was to the camera—odd, but she couldn't even remember what he looked like now. She was glad when the telephone started ringing, before Lee had time to say anything.

It was Lora. He listened to what she had to say, agreed with her unemotionally and held out the receiver to Sharon. 'She wants to speak to you.'

She steeled herself for the touch of his fingers as she took the instrument from him, unable to meet his eyes. 'Hallo, Lora,' she said.

'Just wanted to tell you how impressed Jason and I are with your TV debut,' came the other voice lightly. 'We just caught it.'

'You'll probably be sick of seeing it before long,' Sharon returned with equal lightness. 'At least there's only one of those.'

'Oh well, we don't watch all that much television.' There was a pause before the other girl added on a different note, 'How are you, Sharon?'

She laughed, only too conscious that Lee was listening to her end of the conversation. 'Oh, you know how it is. I'll be glad when these first few weeks are over.'

'Hear, hear!' came the wry response. 'Mind you, Jason is being an absolute angel about the whole thing—morning sickness and all. I only hope that brother of mine is making the same effort.'

'Oh, yes,' said Sharon, 'he is.'

'I am what?' asked Lee casually when she had put the phone down and returned to her seat.

'Lora wanted to know if you were acting with understanding and forbearance,' she said, trying to make a joke of it. 'I told her you were, of course.'

'Of course.' His tone was dry. 'Which other way could I act in the circumstances? It's my fault you're the way you are.'

And mine that you're the way *you* are, she thought in pain. But at least her condition would change with time. Would his?

Richard turned up the following afternoon unannounced.

'I wanted to catch you before Lee came home,' he said, viewing her with an appraising eye. 'I'm glad you two are together again, Sharon.'

'And then there were three.' Her smile held irony. 'You're going to be a grandfather twice over. How does it feel?'

'Good,' he said. 'I'm of an age where I'm ready for it. Lorna isn't quite so sure. She's trying to think of a suitable substitute for "grandmother" which doesn't suggest a white-haired old lady.'

Sharon looked him in the eye. 'How did she take Lee and me getting back together again?'

'I'd say on the whole she was relieved.' He smiled a little, and shrugged. 'Give her time, she'll mellow some day. She was reared to a strict code by parents who never caught up with the twentieth century.'

'It doesn't matter,' said Sharon, and found it was the truth. Whether Lee's mother eventually accepted her or not was of little moment. Lee's was the only regard she either wanted or needed to make her happy.

She got her father-in-law a drink before saying candidly, 'Isn't it time you made up your mind whether Lee is going to take over control of the Company from you or not?'

Richard looked startled for a moment, then he laughed and shook his head. 'You don't believe in skirting round a subject any more, do you?'

'It takes too much time,' she admitted. 'And you still haven't answered the question.'

'All right,' he said, 'I stand corrected. The answer is yes, Lee will take control, if for no other reason than the way he's proved himself these last few weeks. When you left him I more than half expected a return to his former habits, but he didn't. He threw himself into work instead.'

Sharon smiled. 'He said it was a great panacea.'

'It can be—of a kind.' He paused, his regard direct. 'You brought him up with a jerk, Sharon, made him take stock of himself. He's a better man for it. And he'd better make you happy from now on!'

Unfortunately happiness was not a commodity made to order, she reflected wryly after he had gone. It had to be worked at and for. She had thrown away one chance at it, the next one was not going to come as easy—if at all. Perhaps when the baby was here they would find themselves drawn closer again. The fact of pregnancy itself could be a part of Lee's rejection of her.

So make him forget it, urged a hitherto unheard section of her mind. Stop wasting time in useless regrets and *make* him want you again! You have the weapons.

Fired by a sudden sense of new purpose, she took a look at the clock. Lee had said he would be home around seven-thirty tonight. That gave her almost four hours, time enough for almost anything if she put in enough effort.

She heard the car at twenty to eight as she put the final touch to the supper table she had set for two in the music room before the opened french windows. The evening was pure gold, warm and fragrant as a summer evening should be, with a promise in the mackerel sky of more fine weather to come.

Lee paused in his progress across the hall when she appeared, eyes moving down the length of the soft amber velvet lounging gown and back to linger on her subtly highlighted features.

'You look like the Lucci girl,' he said.

Sharon smiled, letting the warmth reach her eyes as well as her lips. 'Only skin deep. I decided it was high time I took a leaf out of her book and dressed for the occasion.'

Dark brows lifted a fraction. 'Is it a special one?'

I hope so, she thought. Oh, God, I hope so! Aloud she said, 'We've been married two months, it seemed we ought to make some gesture. Dinner in fifteen minutes if you want to change.'

'Into something more comfortable, you mean?' The smile was faint and tinged with irony. 'You didn't have to go to this amount of trouble, Sharon.'

'I wanted to.' She refused to let the moment fall flat. 'We're eating in the music room for a change. Don't be too long.'

She left him standing there and went back to the kitchen, biting her lip. If this didn't work there seemed little hope of anything working. Could she bring herself to carry on the way they had been doing for the last few days in that event?

Yes, she acknowledged in sudden conviction. She could because she had to. Love surely didn't depend on Lee's ability to make love to her in return. Supposing he were paralysed and couldn't? Would she stop loving him then? It was too simple an analogy and she knew it. Emotional need was the real crux of the matter.

He came down in exactly fifteen minutes, wearing a bathrobe and nothing else.

'If we're going to relax,' he said, taking his place at the table, 'let's do it wholesale.' He caught her glance and held it, expression full of self-mockery. 'I'll play my part, if that's how you want it.'

It wasn't, but there was little she could say. She had started this and she was going to see it through. She served the meal and ate without appetite, refusing to gain Dutch courage from the wine. If she had to seduce her own husband then that was what she would do. Anything to break down the barriers between them.

Coffee was like a last rite before the event. Oddly enough, conversation had not been stilted up until then, but the putting down of his cup seemed to signal the end of that particular kind of effort—to Lee anyway. He stopped talking and just sat there looking at her. Waiting for the next move?

Sharon made it with her heart beating a slow tattoo against her rib cage, sliding closer along the sofa to put a tentative hand to his face. She could feel the muscle in his cheek contract beneath her fingers—almost flinching away—although his expression didn't alter. She had to force herself to carry on.

'Lee,' she said pleadingly, 'kiss me.'

'Why?' he asked, and it was like a slap in the face,

jerking her head back with the same physical reaction.

'Because I'm asking you to,' she got out through stiff lips. 'Because I want you to.' She paused then, feeling her courage running out before his total lack of response. She took what was left of it in both hands and put her lips to his, moving them slowly and sensuously against the unyielding surface as he had done with her in the past, using every art he had ever shown her to try and reach the man within.

Control was taken from her with a suddenness she had not anticipated, his arms snapping around her back to pull her roughly against him, his mouth becoming the aggressor, the seeker, in its turn. The weight of his body pressed her down into the cushions, his hand finding the fastening at the front of her gown and sliding inside to span the curve of her breast as if that was where it belonged.

'You see?' he murmured ruefully with his lips soft against the hollow of her throat. 'I can't stop at kissing you, Sharon. I want to take you.'

'Then why haven't you?' she whispered, *'Why*, Lee?'

He lifted his head just enough to look at her, searching her face with a slow dawning realisation. 'I didn't think you wanted it,' he said. 'On Sunday night when I brought you home, you started trembling the moment we reached our room.'

'Not with fear.' The same tremor was in her voice now. 'Oh, Lee, I wanted you so much to make love to me. I needed to know you hadn't just brought me back out of a sense of duty. When you walked out on me I wanted to die—I thought I'd lost you completely.' She touched his face with a finger tip, tracing the strong line of his jaw until she reached the point of his chin, then moving upwards to his mouth. 'I love you,' she said softly. 'I'd love you if you hadn't a penny piece in the whole wide world. You've got to believe that.'

'I do.' His own voice was thick. 'God help me, I really do! We've wasted so much time, Sharon. We had all this to start with.'

'No, we didn't,' she denied. 'Not the same. We've both done some changing these last few weeks. The girl you married was a little fool. She didn't have the sense to see further than the end of her nose.'

'And what was I?' he asked, and she smiled.

'You were all I merited. Only I couldn't take it then.'

'But you can now?'

'If it's offered. I can take anything knowing you love me.' She paused there, looking at him with questioning eyes. 'You do, don't you?'

It was his turn to smile. 'Haven't I said so?'

'Not in so many words, no. You never really did.'

'Perhaps because I expect you to be able to read it blazoned across me.' He kissed her with tenderness. 'I love you, Sharon. So much that it goes beyond words.'

'Then show me,' she whispered.

And he did.

Harlequin understands...

the way you feel about love

Harlequin novels are stories of people in love—people like you— and all are beautiful romances, set in exotic faraway places.

What the press says about Harlequin romance fiction...

"...exciting escapism, easy reading, interesting characters and, always, a happy ending.... They are hard to put down."
— *Transcript-Telegram*, Holyoke (Mass.)

"...wholesome fiction...always with an upbeat, happy ending."
— *San Francisco Chronicle*

"...a work of art."
— *The Globe & Mail*, Toronto

"Nothing quite like it has happened since *Gone With the Wind...*"
— *Los Angeles Times*

"...among the top ten..."
— *International Herald-Tribune*, Paris

Harlequin Presents...

The books that let you escape
into the wonderful world of romance!
Trips to exotic places...interesting
plots...meeting memorable people...
the excitement of love....These are
integral parts of Harlequin Presents—
the heartwarming novels read by
women everywhere.

Many early issues are now available.
Choose from this great selection!

Choose from this great selection of exciting Harlequin Presents editions

Relive a great romance...
Harlequin Presents 1980
Complete and mail this coupon today!

Harlequin Reader Service

In U.S.A.
MPO Box 707
Niagara Falls, N.Y. 14302

In Canada
649 Ontario St.
Stratford, Ontario, N5A 6W2

Please send me the following Harlequin Presents novels. I am enclosing my check or money order for $1.50 for each novel ordered, plus 59¢ to cover postage and handling.

☐ 192	☐ 201	☐ 210
☐ 193	☐ 202	☐ 211
☐ 194	☐ 203	☐ 212
☐ 195	☐ 204	☐ 213
☐ 197	☐ 205	☐ 214
☐ 198	☐ 206	☐ 215
☐ 199	☐ 207	☐ 216
☐ 200	☐ 208	☐ 217

Number of novels checked @ $1.50 each = $_____

N.Y. State residents add appropriate sales tax $_____

Postage and handling $_____ .59

TOTAL $_____

I enclose _____
(Please send check or money order. We cannot be responsible for cash sent through the mail.)

Prices subject to change without notice.

NAME _____
(Please Print)

ADDRESS _____

CITY _____

STATE/PROV. _____

ZIP/POSTAL CODE _____

Offer expires February 28, 1981　　　　　　007563170